Praise for *Every Child Can Do Math*

No sooner do you think that you've seen it all when along comes a whole new, wonderfully creative set of beautifully scaffolded math activities. Ban Har, a guiding force behind Singapore Math, with the deft assistance of Lorraine Walker, has assembled what the subtitle accurately calls "deceptively simple" puzzles and problems that provide rich opportunities that disguise problem solving as basic skills practice and basic skills practice as problem solving. The teacher-friendly set-up and the Guided Conversation questions make this a most valuable resource for enacting the mathematical practices of the Common Core.

> —Steve Leinwand
> Principal Research Analyst
> American Institutes for Research

The guided conversations demystify math and encourage new insights. The gentle guidance helps even instinctive math avoiders develop confidence as they search for and justify patterns in the number, geometry, and pre-algebra activities.

> —Douglas Edge, PhD
> Associate Professor (retired)
> National Institute of Education
> Singapore

Every Child Can Do

MATH

Deceptively simple activities to develop mathematical thinking

**Yeap Ban Har, PhD,
and Lorraine Walker**

Crystal Springs BOOKS
SDE
A Division of Staff Development for Educators

Peterborough, New Hampshire

Published by Crystal Springs Books
A division of Staff Development for Educators (SDE)
10 Sharon Road, PO Box 500
Peterborough, NH 03458
1-800-321-0401
www.SDE.com/crystalsprings

Published 2012
Printed in the United States of America
16 15 14 13 12   1 2 3 4 5

ISBN: 978-1-935502-39-5
e-book ISBN: 978-1-935502-40-1

Yeap, Ban Har, 1968- author.
  Every child can do math : deceptively simple activities to develop
mathematical thinking / Yeap Ban Har & Lorraine Walker.
     pages ; cm
  Includes bibliographical references.
  ISBN 978-1-935502-39-5 (alk. paper) -- ISBN 978-1-935502-40-1
  (ebook) 1. Mathematics--Study and teaching (Elementary)--
Activity programs. I. Walker, Lorraine, 1946- author. II.
Title.

  QA135.6.Y43 2012
  372.7--dc23

                       2012019027

Contents

SECTION 1 Number Sense — 15

SECTION 2 Visualization — 81

SECTION ❸ Patterns & Relationships 141

Acknowledgments

One of the key concepts in this book is that good math instruction includes repeated questioning and thoughtful conversation. That's true of this book's development, too. The activities are based on years of classroom experience, so we knew they were strong. But the way the activities are presented grew out of repeated questioning, frequent discussions, and thoughtful input from many people. Thank you to Terra Tarango, Lisa Bingen, and Sharon Smith for seeing the value in these ideas and guiding the publication of this book by SDE and Crystal Springs Books. Thanks also to editor Marianne Knowles, photographer Jenn Phillips-Merrill, creative director Joan Cunningham, and designer Jill Shaffer for translating our vision into reality; to our friend and fellow math educator Ricky Mikelman for reviewing all of these activities for both accuracy and practicality; and to Joan Cunningham for the wonderful cover design. We appreciate your willingness to ask all those questions and to discuss alternatives. And you all deserve A's for visualization and problem-solving, too!

We're also grateful to the models who graciously tried the activities and posed for the photographs with which each activity begins: Riley Bemont, Mia Brady, Hadley Brady, Alex McCall, Lucy Selby, Owen Selby, Jade Tarango, and Rain Tarango. We truly appreciate your help—and the patient support of your parents—in making these activities come to life through the photographs.

We need more than just worksheets to develop mathematical thinkers.

To prepare our students to thrive in a globally connected world, we need to help them become mathematical thinkers. But how do we do that?

It's easy to give students worksheets to practice their math skills. It's easy—but are those worksheets effective? Do the problems presented on the worksheets develop the thinking skills students need in real-life situations and for success in future careers? Do they engage students?

Probably not. Most worksheets are dull and repetitive. They provide practice with computation that could just as easily be done on a calculator. Worksheets have their uses, but they don't develop the kinds of problem-solving and thinking skills that students need.

In the same amount of class time it takes to complete a packet of worksheets, your students can develop a deeper understanding of mathematical concepts—**and have fun doing it!**

Instead of giving students computation worksheets to solve alone, what if we gave them puzzles and non-routine problems that couldn't be solved using a calculator? What if, rather than writing a quick answer to a problem, students had to think up a plan for solving it? What if five different students came up with five different "right" ways to solve the problem, and they had to explain and defend their approaches to each other? And what if this discussion took no more class time than completing a packet of traditional worksheets?

What would happen? We would be taking the first steps toward helping our students develop the ability to:

- make sense of problems and persevere in solving them;
- reason abstractly and quantitatively;
- construct viable arguments and critique the reasoning of others;
- look for and make use of structure;
- look for and express regularity in repeated reasoning.

Worksheets are boring!

These activities help me see and understand the math.

The puzzles really get me thinking!

I like trying out new ways of solving them. This is fun!

Every Child Can Do
MATH

The activities in this book have been chosen to help you take deceptively simple, non-routine problems and use them to engage your students in rich, two-way conversations that develop mathematical thinking.

Recognize these statements? They are part of the Standards for Mathematical Practice described in the Common Core State Standards. They are also at the heart of the non-routine problems contained in this book. Using the activities in this book, your students will:

• go beyond computation and gain good number sense;

• develop the ability to visualize problems and to think through strategies for solving them— not just find the right answer;

• recognize patterns and relationships;

• form the habit of looking for multiple approaches to solving a problem;

• communicate and test their own ideas and ask questions that uncover the mathematical reasoning of others.

You may be wondering, "How can I help students do these things? I don't think this way about math myself!" It's true that many of us were taught to understand math as a set of procedures. We were told that "Ours is not to question why—just invert and multiply." We learned to find the right answer, but we were led to believe, erroneously, that there is only one right way to find it.

This book will help both you and your students develop your mathematical thinking, so you can better understand the reasoning behind the math. Along the way, you may find yourself enjoying math in a way you haven't before— you may discover that math really doesn't have to be that hard. It's even fun! And when *you're* having fun, your students will, too. As their enthusiasm for math grows, so will their skills.

As you work through the activities, you'll see that **every child can do math.**

How This Book Is Organized

The activities in this book develop five key mathematical competencies: number sense, visualization, recognizing patterns & relationships, communication, and questioning. The book is organized into three sections that focus on three of these areas.

SECTION 1
Number Sense

SECTION 2
Visualization

SECTION 3
Patterns & Relationships

Each section includes multiple activities that provide rich experience solving the kinds of problems that develop top-notch mathematical thinkers.

The other two key competencies, communication and questioning, are central to problem-solving in all branches of mathematics, and, therefore, are embedded throughout all activities in the book. Though the activities within each section emphasize one particular aspect of mathematical thinking, the skills developed overlap a good deal.

Sections

Each section begins with a classroom scenario that models the kind of higher-order, flexible mathematical thinking that many students lack—but which your students will develop by engaging in the activities in the section.

SECTION 1

Activities 1–8

Number Sense

Number sense means understanding more than just how to compute.

SECTION 1

Number Sense

In this example, we see that both Sam and Reena have the ability to do basic computation, essentially the same thing an inexpensive calculator can do. But we also see that Reena has more—she has number sense, a conceptual understanding of numbers and operations. Reena's number sense lets her see ways to manipulate numbers in order to simplify a computation. She is comfortable enough with numbers that she can play with them. She does far more than follow procedures—she understands the meaning behind the math.

Our goal for teaching mathematics must be to help Sam do what Reena is doing. The activities, games, and puzzles in this section are designed to help Sam, and others like him, develop number sense.

Why Does Number Sense Matter?

Reena does 29×6 by first finding 30×6 mentally. Then she subtracts 6 from 180 to find 29×6. Reena sees 29×6 as $(30 \times 6) - (1 \times 6)$, which makes it easier for her to find the answer. Reena has number sense.

Sam solves this same problem, 29×6. First, he writes it down. Then he thinks "6 times 9 is 54." He places the 5 above the tens column and writes down the 4. Next he thinks "6 times 2 is 12, plus 5 is 17." Sam gets the same answer as Reena, 174. Sam is not wrong, but does he truly understand what he has done?

$(30 \times 6) - 6$ $\begin{array}{r}29\\ \times 6\end{array}$ $9 \times 6 = 54$, carry the 5 …

Reena's number sense helps her with subtraction, too. Reena looks at $24 - 18$, switches the numbers in her head to $26 - 20$, and quickly gets 6. Sam looks at $24 - 18$ and rewrites it vertically. Sam gets 14 for his answer. Whoops. Sam has learned a procedure, but he is using it incorrectly. If Sam develops number sense, then he'll know that 14 is too large to be the correct answer.

$26 - 20 = 6$ $24 - 18 = ?$ $\begin{array}{r}24\\ -18\\ \hline 14\end{array}$

Next the students are told that each letter in the following puzzle stands for a digit. The same letter always stands for the same digit. Different letters stand for different digits. They must find what numbers the letters equal.

Oh! The "L" must be a "1." $\begin{array}{r}\text{LIVE}\\ \times 9\\ \hline \text{EVIL}\end{array}$???

Reena, using her number sense, sees that L has to be the digit 1 for the product to be a 4-digit number. She is on the way to solving the whole puzzle ($1089 \times 9 = 9801$). Sam's computation skills can't help him solve this nonroutine problem. If he learns to understand numbers as Reena does, such problems will be possible and even fun. His new number sense will transfer to solving nonroutine problems in everyday life.

16   Section 1 / Number Sense

Activities

The activities within each section develop students' number sense, visualization skills, or understanding of patterns and relationships, while fostering communication and questioning skills.

A brief introduction explains how your students will benefit from the activity.

You can quickly check whether an activity is appropriate for your students' readiness level.

At a glance, identify the words your students will need to know.

Where appropriate, the Rules of the Road briefly summarize the instructions you'll be giving students.

Quickly scan this information to see what you need to plan for the activity—in terms of both time and materials.

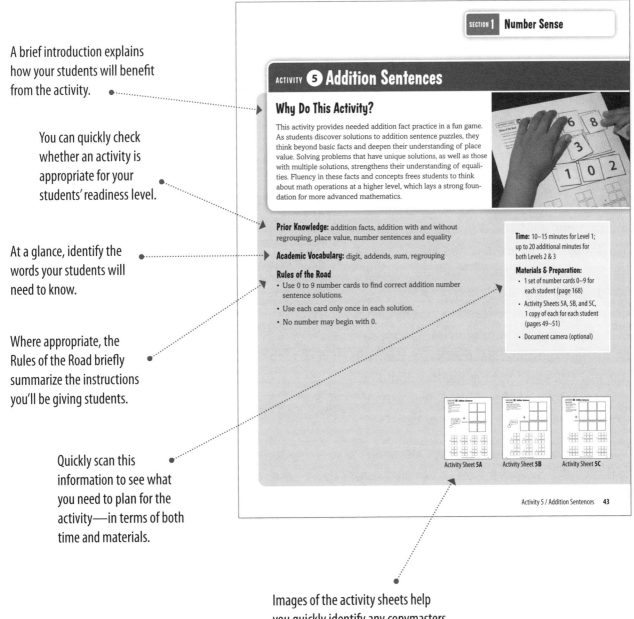

SECTION 1   Number Sense

ACTIVITY 5   Addition Sentences

Why Do This Activity?

This activity provides needed addition fact practice in a fun game. As students discover solutions to addition sentence puzzles, they think beyond basic facts and deepen their understanding of place value. Solving problems that have unique solutions, as well as those with multiple solutions, strengthens their understanding of equalities. Fluency in these facts and concepts frees students to think about math operations at a higher level, which lays a strong foundation for more advanced mathematics.

Prior Knowledge: addition facts, addition with and without regrouping, place value, number sentences and equality

Academic Vocabulary: digit, addends, sum, regrouping

Rules of the Road
- Use 0 to 9 number cards to find correct addition number sentence solutions.
- Use each card only once in each solution.
- No number may begin with 0.

Time: 10–15 minutes for Level 1; up to 20 additional minutes for both Levels 2 & 3

Materials & Preparation:
- 1 set of number cards 0–9 for each student (page 168)
- Activity Sheets 5A, 5B, and 5C, 1 copy of each for each student (pages 49–51)
- Document camera (optional)

Activity Sheet **5A**   Activity Sheet **5B**   Activity Sheet **5C**

Activity 5 / Addition Sentences   **43**

Images of the activity sheets help you quickly identify any copymasters you need to reproduce.

How to Use the Activities

Are you wondering where to begin? In most cases you can dip in and work with any activity in the book that meshes well with your curriculum. In a few cases, the text notes where it's a good idea to do one activity before another.

Using the Activity Levels

Multiple activity levels give you options for differentiation. For any activity, we recommend that you do Level 1 as a class. You'll notice that even at Level 1, many of the questions encourage students to think about what they are doing, in order to deepen their mastery and comprehension of a math operation or concept. Supported by the Guided Conversation suggestions in the activity, all of your students should be able to participate in—and all will benefit from—Level 1 questions and discussions.

You can build on your students' success with Level 1 by moving on to Levels 2 and 3 to help them further develop their understanding of a concept. Levels 2 and 3 may also be done in a whole-group setting, or you may assign the levels to small groups if some students in the class are ready to move on. Don't worry if you can't continue with Levels 2 and 3 right away—in fact, waiting a few days or even weeks can help students solidify their thinking skills. Waiting also reinforces the idea that students are expected to master the strategy that they've gained during the activity and use it again. You will, however, want to quickly review what students completed in Level 1 before beginning Level 2 or 3.

Don't be afraid to push all of your students on to the higher levels. These activities are so engaging and so motivating that your students will want to do more—and with your support, all students can be successful.

Levels Within Activities

You'll notice that each activity has two or three levels. At all levels, the emphasis is on communication, questioning, and thinking. The three activity levels are related to the levels in Bloom's Taxonomy:

Activity Level	Develops These Levels from Bloom's Taxonomy
1	Remember, Understand
2	Apply, Analyze
3	Evaluate, Create

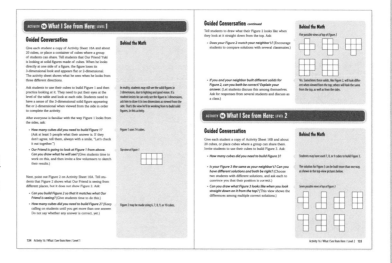

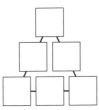
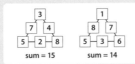
Each Activity Is Divided into Two Parts

Guided Conversation describes how to present the puzzles, games, and activities and provides suggestions for guiding classroom conversation about them.

Behind the Math explains the thinking and reasoning behind various approaches to solving a problem and provides answers.

Guiding the Conversation

Math shouldn't be learned in silence. The more your students can talk about math, communicate their thinking, and hear the ideas of other students, the deeper and longer-lasting their understanding will be. The games, puzzles, and activities in this book offer great opportunities for your students to discuss math. You can enhance those opportunities through regular use of the following approaches.

Ask open-ended questions. Asking how a student figured out the answer is far more interesting and engaging than simply asking for the right answer—especially when you encourage students to share multiple ways to find the same answer.

Wait for answers. Allow plenty of wait time before you call on any student for an answer. Even if one student is eager to answer quickly, others may need time to think through their responses. Since the goal is to encourage thinking for all of your students, make sure all of your students get the time they need.

Guiding the Conversation *continued*

Call on many students. When you ask a question, even one that has a one-word answer, avoid saying whether the first answer is right or wrong. Instead, ask the same question of four or five students. If the second or third student says, "My answer is the same as hers," just smile and say, "Please, I want to hear your response." If everyone gives the same correct answer, say something like, "You appear to agree that this is the answer." If they all give you the same wrong answer, you might say, "Let's check the answer to make sure it works." The goal is to encourage students to think about each other's responses, rather than turning to the teacher to provide the answer.

Encourage multiple ways of solving problems. When students describe more than one approach to solving a particular problem, they are showing that they are learning to think mathematically. Encourage this by making a list, where everyone can see it, of the different methods students used to solve the same problem. It doesn't have to be long—just jot down a couple of key words that describe each different method that students suggest.

Have students talk with each other. You won't always have time to hear everyone's solution. The next best thing is to ask students to share their solutions with their neighbors. What if they don't agree on the solution? That's great—it's an opportunity to explain to their neighbor the process they used to find the solution. Together, they can determine whether either of them has an approach that works. If not, they can work together to find one that does.

ACTIVITY 7 Multiplication Sentences: LEVEL 2

Guided Conversation

Hand out Activity Sheet 7B (and sets of number cards 0 to 9, if you haven't already). Ask students to use the number cards to find and record solutions for the multiplication sentence on the activity sheet.

Remind them to record solutions at the bottom of the sheet.

After students have worked for a while, ask:

- *This is the product of a 2-digit number and a 1-digit number. What has to happen in order to get a 3-digit answer?* (Even if the first person gives you a correct answer, call on other students to explain their thinking. If they say they did it the same way as the previous person, tell them you'd still like to hear them describe the process they used. Sometimes they may restate it slightly differently, and that's a good thing because it helps other students to catch on to the concept. Plus, by pushing for them to share, it lets them know you really want to hear what *they* are thinking.)

Ask some of the following questions. Each time, allow several people to share their thinking.

- *Can 0 be a digit in either of the factors? How do you know?*

- *What is the least (smallest) product you can find?* (If students need help getting started, suggest that they start by determining what is the least 3-digit number and then considering if they can find factors to produce this number.)

Behind the Math

There are many possible solutions. Encourage students to check each other's work if they want assurance that their solutions are correct.

In order to have a product that is a 3-digit number, some regrouping has to occur.

Zero can't be used in either of the factors. If it were, then 0 would be needed in the product, and only one 0 card is available.

In solving these puzzles, it can be helpful to start out with guess-and-check, focusing on the final product you want. For example, when trying to find the least 3-digit answer, consider what the options are: 100, 101, 102 ... As you look for factors that yield this product, you'll find the first one that works is $53 \times 2 = 106$. This is a more organized, systematic approach to finding the answer than random guessing.

64   Activity 7 / Multiplication Sentences / Level 2

Give hints instead of answers. Introduce your class to a special math expert who can help them think through a problem. In this book, we call this expert Our Friend Yuki (pronounced YOU-key), but you can give him any name you like. When students get stuck, let Yuki come to their rescue. Our Friend gives hints of just a few words, modeling the kind of thinking that is helpful for solving the problem at hand. Draw Our Friend and tell students what he's saying; then wait for answers. Call on many students, and let them explain how Yuki's hint helped them figure out how to solve the problem.

Be ready for your students to come up with approaches that aren't included here. Once they start thinking mathematically, they'll uncover multiple ways to find the right answer. If your students can explain their thinking, and the approach consistently solves a puzzle, then they may be right—even if their answer isn't in the book!

Activity Sheets

The activity sheets are not worksheets! We've included activity sheets when appropriate, to support students in manipulating materials, recording solutions, or otherwise working with the math challenge while you are discussing it as a class.

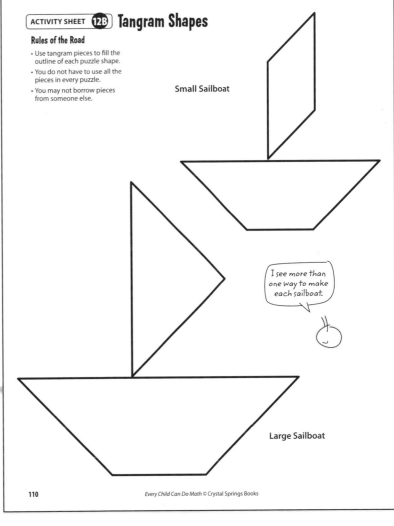

ACTIVITY SHEET **12B** Tangram Shapes

Rules of the Road
- Use tangram pieces to fill the outline of each puzzle shape.
- You do not have to use all the pieces in every puzzle.
- You may not borrow pieces from someone else.

Small Sailboat

I see more than one way to make each sailboat.

Large Sailboat

110   *Every Child Can Do Math* © Crystal Springs Books

I give hints.

Our friend Yuki helps me think about the the problem in new ways!

Looking Behind the Math

The "Guided Conversation" column helps you generate meaningful conversations about math with your students—conversations that will help them build real understanding of complex mathematical concepts. The parallel column, "Behind the Math," provides answers right at point of use and offers deeper explanations to support your understanding of the concepts. You'll also find strategies for effective instruction.

"Behind the Math" explains the "why" behind the solutions so you will be able to:

- respond to students' questions
- help them make connections
- support them as they look for alternative approaches to solving the puzzles and problems

"Behind the Math" gives you the support you need to help your students become powerful mathematical thinkers.

Talking it over with my classmates helps me understand the math concepts.

Guided Conversation

Show students Our Friend's thinking about the problem 29 × 4. Ask:

- *Where did Our Friend get 120? Did he multiply? What did he multiply?*
- *How come Our Friend is subtracting to solve a multiplication problem? How does that work?*

29 × 4 = ? 120 − 4 = 116!

Write the problem shown below, and then tell students that Our Friend was going to do this problem on his calculator. But Our Friend discovered that the 9 button was broken. How did he do this problem on his calculator without using the 9 button?

```
  1234
×   59
     ?
```

If students get stuck after you've given them plenty of time to think this through, tell them Our Friend wants to give them a hint.

Draw Yuki.

60

Ask:

- *What do you think Our Friend means by saying, "60"?*
- *How does he use 60?*
- *How can Our Friend find 59 groups of 1234 after finding 60 groups of 1234?* (As needed, point out that Our Friend is using a calculator for these problems. Yes, even Our Friend Yuki uses a calculator sometimes!)

Behind the Math

Our Friend got 120 by multiplying 30 by 4. Why would he do that? He knows that 29 × 4 can be thought of as 29 groups of 4. He knows 30 groups of 4 is 120 (30 × 4 = 120). But he also knows that he wants only 29 groups of 4, so he needs to take away (subtract) 1 group of 4 from that product. So, 120 − 4 gives him the answer to 29 × 4.

With practice, most students can do problems like 29 × 4 in their heads. There is no need to grind through the traditional algorithm of multiplying 9 and 4, writing down the 6 and "carrying" the 3, then multiplying 2 × 4 and adding 3. Yes, you can get the answer that way, but why do it? Our Friend's methods are faster, and they instill a deeper, stronger understanding of numbers.

Our Friend decides to change 1234 × 59 to 1234 × 60 so he doesn't need to use the 9 key:

1234 × 60 = 74,040

Since Our Friend isn't really looking for the answer to 60 groups of 1234, he then subtracts 1234 from the product so he ends up with 59 groups:

74,040 − 1234 = 72,806

One of your students may take a different approach, such as saying, "Multiply 58 × 1234 and add another group of 1234 to that product." This is perfectly fine, and the fact that students see more than one way to solve the problem shows that they are developing good number sense. Encourage students to describe these multiplication problems as a certain number of groups of another number.

Guided Conversation *continued*

Tell students that Our Friend has another way to make multiplying easier. Ask them to figure out what he's doing. Talk students through the answer until they understand.

84 × 5 840 ÷ 2

Tell students that Our Friend has a third way to multiply. He understands how to find area, so when he saw 743 × 25, he drew an area diagram. Draw the problem and the diagram for students, and then discuss using the questions below.

743 × 25 = ?

	700	40	3
20			
5			

- *Can you figure out what to put in the empty boxes in Our Friend's diagram?*
- *How does Our Friend's diagram help him find the answer to this multiplication problem?*

Behind the Math

Our Friend knows that 5 groups of 84 is the same as half of 10 groups of 84. Ten groups of 84 is easy—it's 840. Half of that is also easy—it's 420. So, 5 groups of 84 equals 420 (or 84 × 5 = 420). At first, it may seem wasteful to go through so many extra steps to reach an answer, but the time invested in helping students to understand this kind of thinking pays off. Once students can think flexibly about numbers, even problems involving large numbers become easy.

	700	40	3
20	14,000	800	60
5	3,500	200	15

17,500 + 1,000 + 75 = 18,575

Our Friend's diagram is an area model. It's an organized way to show all the partial products that make up the problem he is doing. The area model shows how to multiply factors using expanded notation. Expanded notation lets Our Friend multiply multiples of 10s, 100s, and so on, which is easier than multiplying digits. It also makes the problem very visual, and it's easier to keep track of the value of each digit (ones, tens, hundreds) in both factors.

When Our Friend adds all these partial products together, he will have the answer to the original problem (743 × 25 = 18,575).

Guided Conversation

In Level 3, the alternatives to traditional algorithms use number properties that students may or may not have learned yet. But seeing the properties used in the context of Our Friend Yuki's solutions will give students an excellent foundation for making these properties their own, whenever these number properties are formally introduced.

When to Use This Book

When you use these activities in your classroom is up to you. There is no right or wrong way to incorporate them into your class routine.

You might consider beginning your daily math time with one level of an activity. Or you could complete a few each week at a special time set aside for "The Weekly Challenge" or "Problem of the Week."

Some activities can be springboards for further practice. Do an activity together as a class and then change the numbers or shapes used in the puzzle to create a different version. Once students know how to do the activity, you can use that other version in math centers, as an anchor activity for students who finish classwork quickly, or as a take-home activity. There is really no end to how many times you can change these puzzles and activities to create new versions.

Initially, the activities might take longer than you expect because both you and your students are getting used to these types of problems. But don't be tempted to skimp on time for questions and discussions—that's where the true value of the activities lies.

On the other hand, once you and your class become acclimated to this approach, you may be able to progress more quickly on occasion. For this reason, we recommend that you read through all the levels before you begin an activity. Rarely would you want to cover more than one level of one activity at a time, but you want to be prepared in case students complete a level quickly and there is time to move on.

We do recommend that you find a way to include these activities on a regular basis. Students need to do this kind of thinking frequently in order to develop higher-order skills and get ready for algebra.

And that means that the sooner you get started, the better. It's time to move beyond traditional worksheets that teach children to memorize procedures. Dive in, encourage your students with lots of questions, and guide them through the activities. If you use this book on a regular basis, your students will learn far more than rote calculation. They truly will become mathematical thinkers.

> You can make mathematics more accessible, intuitive, and fun.
>
> Every child can do math!
>
> — Yeap Ban Har

Activity Connections to Common Core State Standards for Mathematics

Standards for Mathematical Practice	*Every Child Can Do Math* Activities
1. Make sense of problems and persevere in solving them.	1, 2, 3, 4, 5, 6, 7, 8, 9, 10, 11, 12, 13, 14, 15, 16, 17, 18, 19, 20, 21
2. Reason abstractly and quantitatively.	1, 2, 3, 4, 5, 6, 7, 8, 9, 10, 11, 12, 13, 14, 15, 16, 17, 18, 19, 20, 21
3. Construct viable arguments and critique the reasoning of others.	3, 4, 5, 6, 7, 8, 10, 11, 13, 14, 16, 17, 18, 19, 20, 21
4. Model with mathematics.	1, 2, 8, 9, 10, 11, 12, 13, 14, 15, 16, 17, 19, 20, 21
5. Use appropriate tools strategically.	9, 10, 11, 12, 13, 14, 16, 17
6. Attend to precision.	1, 2, 3, 4, 5, 6, 7, 8, 9, 10, 11, 12, 13
7. Look for and make use of structure.	1, 2, 3, 4, 5, 6, 7, 8, 9, 10, 11, 12, 13, 14, 15, 16, 17, 18, 19, 20, 21
8. Look for and express regularity in repeated reasoning.	2, 3, 4, 5, 6, 7, 8, 9, 10, 17, 18, 19, 20, 21

Activity Connections to 21st Century Student Outcomes

The Partnership for 21st Century Skills: Learning and Innovation Skills	*Every Child Can Do Math* Activities
Critical Thinking	2, 3, 4, 5, 6, 7, 8, 9, 10, 11, 13, 14, 15, 16, 17, 18, 19, 20, 21
Communication	1, 3, 4, 5, 6, 7, 8, 9, 10, 11, 12, 13, 14, 16, 17, 18, 19, 20, 21
Collaboration	1, 2, 3, 4, 5, 6, 7, 8, 9, 10, 11, 14, 16, 17, 19, 20, 21
Creativity	3, 4, 8, 9, 10, 11, 12, 13, 14, 17, 18, 19, 20, 21

Activities 1-8

Number Sense

Number sense means understanding more than just how to compute.

Number Sense

In this example, we see that both Sam and Reena have the ability to do basic computation, essentially the same thing an inexpensive calculator can do. But we also see that Reena has more—she has number sense, a conceptual understanding of numbers and operations. Reena's number sense lets her see ways to manipulate numbers in order to simplify a computation. She is comfortable enough with numbers that she can play with them. She does far more than follow procedures—she understands the meaning behind the math.

Our goal for teaching mathematics must be to help Sam do what Reena is doing. The activities, games, and puzzles in this section are designed to help Sam, and others like him, develop number sense.

Why Does Number Sense Matter?

Reena does 29×6 by first finding 30×6 mentally. Then she subtracts 6 from 180 to find 29×6. Reena sees 29×6 as $(30 \times 6) - (1 \times 6)$, which makes it easier for her to find the answer. Reena has number sense.

Sam solves this same problem, 29×6. First, he writes it down. Then he thinks "6 times 9 is 54." He places the 5 above the tens column and writes down the 4. Next he thinks "6 times 2 is 12, plus 5 is 17." Sam gets the same answer as Reena, 174. Sam is not wrong, but does he truly understand what he has done?

$(30 \times 6) - 6$

$$\begin{array}{r} 29 \\ \times\ 6 \\ \end{array}$$

$9 \times 6 = 54,$ carry the 5 . . .

Reena's number sense helps her with subtraction, too. Reena looks at $24 - 18$, switches the numbers in her head to $26 - 20$, and quickly gets 6. Sam looks at $24 - 18$ and rewrites it vertically. Sam gets 14 for his answer. Whoops. Sam has learned a procedure, but he is using it incorrectly. If Sam develops number sense, then he'll know that 14 is too large to be the correct answer.

$26 - 20 = 6$

$24 - 18 = ?$

$$\begin{array}{r} 24 \\ -\ 18 \\ \hline 14 \end{array}$$

Next the students are told that each letter in the following puzzle stands for a digit. The same letter always stands for the same digit. Different letters stand for different digits. They must find what numbers the letters equal.

Oh! The "L" must be a "1."

$$\begin{array}{r} \text{LIVE} \\ \times\ 9 \\ \hline \text{EVIL} \end{array}$$

???

Reena, using her number sense, sees that L has to be the digit 1 for the product to be a 4-digit number. She is on the way to solving the whole puzzle ($1089 \times 9 = 9801$). Sam's computation skills can't help him solve this nonroutine problem. If he learns to understand numbers as Reena does, such problems will be possible and even fun. His new number sense will transfer to solving nonroutine problems in everyday life.

ACTIVITY **1** Number Facts

Why Do This Activity?

These games provide fun ways to have students build mental math skills and fluency in basic math facts. Students will be so engaged that they'll hardly notice you are also solidifying their understanding of the relationship between addition and subtraction, as well as the relationship between multiplication and division—key elements in developing strong number sense.

Prior Knowledge: addition and subtraction facts; may also be used for multiplication

Academic Vocabulary: sum, addend, difference, product

Rules of the Road

- This game is for 3 players.

- Players 1 and 2 draw cards and hold them to their foreheads. They can see each other's cards, but not their own. (No peeking!)

- Player 3 announces the sum of the 2 cards.

- The first player to correctly say the number on his own card wins that round.

- If Player 3 makes a math mistake, then no one wins that round.

- Players switch roles after several rounds.

- Levels 2 and 3 offer variations with more players and different operations.

Time: 15 minutes per level

Materials & Preparation:
- 1 set of number cards 1–10 made from index cards for each group
- Decks of playing cards with face cards removed may be used instead.

Guided Conversation

Invite three students to help you demonstrate the game for the class. Take the 6 and 5 number cards from one of the decks and hold them facedown. Tell Players 1 and 2 you're going to count to three. On three, they each take a card and quickly hold it to their foreheads. They can't see their own card, but they can see their friend's card. The third player can see both cards. He announces, "The sum of the cards is . . . 11." As soon as this is announced, Players 1 and 2 say, "My number is . . ." The first student to say this with the correct answer wins that round. Player 3, the announcer, confirms who the winner is. If the announcer makes a math mistake, then no one wins the round.

Divide students into groups of three. Place a stack of cards facedown in the middle of each group and let them play. Have players switch roles every 5 or 10 rounds so everyone gets a chance at playing and at being the announcer.

Once everyone has played the game, come together again for discussion. Ask:

- *What are some strategies you used to find the unknown number?* (Allow several students to share the strategies they used. Write all the strategies in a list on the board.)

If no one mentions number bonds or part-whole drawings, ask about them:

- *Did anyone see a number bond in her head? What did it look like?*

Behind the Math

Be careful not to say "The first student to guess the card he is holding wins." There is no need to *guess* in these games. The point is that students can *know* by using addition and subtraction facts.

Observe students as they play the game to get a sense of who might need more help with instructions or is slower with the mental math facts. You may wish to adjust groupings so students do not get frustrated if the other players are finding answers at a very different pace. (If you find that's the case, simply say it's time to switch groups around and do it, without saying why.)

Writing the students' strategies on the board helps all students see that you appreciate that they use different approaches to find the same result.

Guided Conversation *continued*

- *Did anyone think of a part-whole drawing?* (Draw bonds and part-whole drawings for your students if they are not familiar with them.)

If appropriate for your students, ask:

- *Did anyone picture algebraic expressions?*

After a good discussion, say:

- *I'm confused. The announcer said, "The sum of the cards is . . . ," but a lot of you said you subtracted. How can that be?*

Behind the Math

11	
5	?

$$5 + x = 11$$
$$x = 11 - 5$$
$$x = 6$$

The discussion about using subtraction to find a missing addend encourages the understanding that addition and subtraction are the same process in reverse. Understandings like this are central to developing strong number sense and help to lay the foundation for algebraic thinking.

ACTIVITY ① Number Facts: LEVEL 2

Guided Conversation

A variation on the addition game played in Level 1 is to use groups of 4. Players 1, 2, and 3 draw cards, and Player 4 announces the sum of the three cards.

Invite 4 students to help you demonstrate for the class. Hand cards 3, 4, and 10 (facedown) to three of the students to hold on their foreheads. (Remind them that when they're playing on their own, they'll just draw cards from the deck when the announcer counts to three.) Have the fourth student announce, "The sum is 17." Then name the person holding the 3 card, without saying what card that person is holding. Ask:

- *What can [Name] know for sure?* (Give students in the class a chance to think about this, before allowing answers.)

- *Is this enough information for [Name] to figure out the number on her card?* (Show how to find the number using both addition and subtraction.)

Form groups of 4 and let students play. Check in with groups and encourage players to explain how they are figuring out what cards they have on their foreheads. Encourage some students to write down the sums and differences they are using.

Behind the Math

The student holding the 3 card knows that the total sum is 17. She also can figure out that the sum of the other 2 cards is 14 (4 + 10). So yes, she can use this information to figure out that she has the 3 card because $4 + 10 + 3 = 17$.

Other ways to think about it:

$$17 - 10 - 4 = 3$$

$$17 - (10 + 4) = 3$$

Guided Conversation *continued*

If students need practice with multiplication fact fluency, have them play the game in groups of three as described in Level 1, but instead of Player 3 stating the sum of the 2 cards, that player should say, "The product of the numbers is . . ."

Again, when students have had ample time to play the game, ask them to share some of the strategies they used to find the missing numbers. Suppose one of your students says he divided. Ask him:

- *Why did you divide if we're talking about the product of 2 numbers?*

Behind the Math

As with the addition activities in Level 1, these strategy discussions give you great opportunities to get your students to recognize the relationship between multiplication and division.

ACTIVITY **1** Number Facts: LEVEL **3**

Guided Conversation

In this variation, students find a number when 1 number and the difference between the 2 numbers are known. This activity has a bit of a twist for students to figure out, so start playing it as a class.

Ask 2 students to come forward. Give the 5 card to one student and the 7 card to the other to hold on their foreheads, as before. Ask the rest of the class to be announcers. Tell them to announce the difference—in this case, they'll say "The difference is 2."

Ask the player with the 5 card to say his number. Next, ask the player with the 7 card to say her number. (Each player has 2 possible correct answers, using the information given.) Ask the class:

- *Why are they getting more than one answer?*
- *What can the announcer say to make sure that there is only one correct answer in this version of the game?*

Encourage students to come up with two ways that the announcer can provide the information that players need.

Give students a chance to play in groups of three.

Behind the Math

Presumably the player with the 5 card (who can see only the 7) will say his card is 9 or 5. The player with the 7 card (who can see only the 5) might say her card is 7 or 3. Students should conclude that knowing the difference is not enough to know the correct answer. The players also need to know which number is greater.

The announcer will need to say, "The difference is 2 and [Name] has the smaller number." The announcer can switch it up and sometimes say who has the larger number, rather than the smaller number. Once the players know which card has the smaller or larger number, they can narrow their answers to one number.

ACTIVITY 2 Cross Number Puzzle

Why Do This Activity?

Students will enjoy completing these puzzles according to specific rules while they are practicing their single-digit addition facts. But these relatively simple-looking puzzles also allow you to push your students to new levels that require higher-order thinking. By creating organized lists of possible solutions, students will start to recognize patterns emerging among the numbers.

Prior Knowledge: addition facts to 20

Academic Vocabulary: sum, horizontal, vertical, consecutive numbers, addend

Rules of the Road

- Use number cards 1 to 9 to find correct solutions to the cross-shaped addition puzzle.

- Each number card may be used only once in each solution.

- Sum of the three horizontal boxes must equal the sum of the three vertical boxes.

- Solutions that have the same sums are the same solution. Solutions with different sums are different solutions.

Time: 15–20 minutes for each level

Materials & Preparation:

- 1 set of number cards 1–9 for each student (page 168)

- Activity Sheet 2, 1 copy for each student, (page 28) plus some extras

- Document camera (optional)

Activity Sheet 2

Guided Conversation

Give each student a set of number cards 1 to 9 and a copy of Activity Sheet 2. Point out the cross puzzle boxes at the top of the activity sheet. Explain to the students that they'll place number cards in the boxes to find solutions to the puzzle. Using cards lets them work more quickly than writing, and they don't need to erase. Once they've found a solution that works, they'll write it in one of the small puzzles at the bottom of the sheet.

Tell students that their first challenge is to arrange the number cards 1 to 5 so that the sum of the three horizontal boxes is equal to the sum of the three vertical boxes.

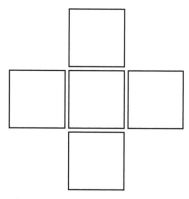

Allow students plenty of time to practice. If some are struggling, you might suggest they start out working with a partner.

Confirm that all students have at least one answer to the puzzle, then ask:

- *What is the sum for each of the three boxes?*

As soon as students realize that some people have different answers, ask them:

- *Can you find a different sum than the one you already have, using the same numbers?*

Give students time to find alternate solutions using numbers 1 to 5, and then ask:

- *What other sums did you find that worked?*

Behind the Math

Once this has been modeled as a class activity, you'll find it also works well for individual activities and for math centers.

Using digits 1 to 5, students might discover there are three unique possible sums.

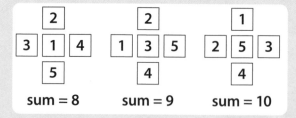

It may help to point out the third Rule of the Road: *Solutions that have the same sums are the same solution. Solutions with different sums are different solutions.* As needed, guide students to recognize that 2 puzzles with the same numbers in each row are the same solution, even if the numbers are in a different order. Likewise, 2 puzzles with the horizontal and vertical rows reversed are the same solution.

Guided Conversation *continued*

Have students try other sets of five consecutive single-digit numbers. Hand out more copies of Activity Sheet 2 as needed. Ask:

- *Can you solve this puzzle using the numbers 2 to 6?*
- *Can you solve it using 3 to 7?*
- *How about 4 to 8?*
- *How many different sums can you find for each set of numbers?*

You may choose to do these sets as a class one at a time, or you may divide the class into groups, each working with a different set of five consecutive numbers.

Save the solutions students come up with because they may be used in the Level 3 activity.

Behind the Math

For each of the other sets of five consecutive numbers, there are three different sums.

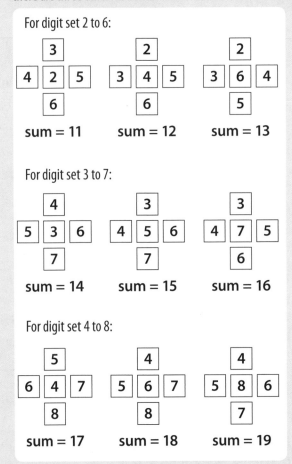

For digit set 2 to 6:

sum = 11   sum = 12   sum = 13

For digit set 3 to 7:

sum = 14   sum = 15   sum = 16

For digit set 4 to 8:

sum = 17   sum = 18   sum = 19

ACTIVITY ② Cross Number Puzzle: LEVEL 2

Guided Conversation

When students are trying to come up with all the different solutions for the Level 1 puzzles, many will use the guess-and-check method. In Level 2, your goal is to lead them toward a more systematic way of reaching an answer.

Ask students to help you as you work through this problem together. Write the numbers 5, 4, 3, 2, and 1 in a column so the whole class can see. Point to the number 5 and ask:

- *What other two numbers, plus this number, 5, add up to 8?* (If the number 3 is suggested, confirm that 5 + 3 = 8, then remind students that three numbers are needed to solve the puzzle and ask what two numbers add up to 3.)

Behind the Math

Sample charts for a systemic approach are shown on page 24.

$5 + 2 + 1 = 8$

Guided Conversation *continued*

Next, point to the number 4 and repeat the question:

- *What other two numbers, plus this number, 4, add up to 8?*

Continue filling in the chart for 3, 2, and 1. You'll probably have to fill in most of this first list yourself, but keep asking students for their assistance. When you are finished, have students help you review the chart. Tell them you want to erase any repeated answers. Ask:

- *Are these solutions all different, or are any of them the same sums with their numbers in different orders?* (In other words, if you list 1 + 2 + 5, you don't need to write 2 + 5 + 1, as both have the same addends. Erase sums until you have only unique examples left in the chart.)

Draw the blank cross-shaped puzzle grid for everyone to see. Say to students that they're looking for two different sums of three numbers that both add up to 8. Look at the blank cross puzzle and the completed chart and ask:

- *Do these two sums have an addend in common?*
- *Where in the puzzle do you think that common number would go?*

Based on how students are doing, either use this approach to try the next problem as a class, or allow students to try it on their own. Tell students to create a chart like the one you just did, but ask them to use numbers 4, 5, 6, 7, and 8 and look for three addends with a sum of 19. After they've completed the chart, students may use that information to complete the cross puzzle.

Remember, your goal is to get students to see that there is a systematic approach to finding a solution, rather than using guess-and-check. When students are ready, invite them to try the following problem. Assign half the class to use a chart and the other half to use guess-and-check.

- *Can you use the numbers 5, 6, 7, 8, and 9 in the puzzle and have the sum equal 23?* (Give students enough time to work on this before calling for a class discussion.)

Behind the Math

Here's what your final chart should look like. There are only two unique combinations of three addends whose sums equal 8.

Consecutive Numbers	Combinations for 8
5	5 + 2 + 1
4	4 + 3 + 1
3	(no new combinations)
2	(no new combinations)
1	(no new combinations)

The common addend is 1, so the number 1 must go in the middle box. That way it is part of both the vertical and horizontal sums.

Here's the final chart for 4, 5, 6, 7, and 8 with a sum of 19. The common addend is 8, so that goes in the center square of the puzzle.

Consecutive Numbers	Combinations for 19
8	8 + 7 + 4, 8 + 6 + 5
7	(no new combinations)
6	(no new combinations)
5	(no new combinations)
4	(no new combinations)

The only combination that totals 23 using these five numbers is 9 + 8 + 6. One combination is not enough to fill both lines in the puzzle.

Consecutive Numbers	Combinations for 23
9	9 + 8 + 6
8	(no new combinations)
7	(no combinations)
6	(no new combinations)
5	(no combinations)

Guided Conversation *continued*

Discuss the results as a class. Students using the chart method should realize that this problem has no solution. Students using guess-and-check might keep moving numbers around thinking they just haven't found the right combination yet, without realizing that they are wasting their time.

Behind the Math

This realization—that taking time to organize data in a chart saves time in the long run—is hugely important. Remind students that this chart is easy to complete when numbers are arranged in an organized way, such as listing the five consecutive numbers in order in the first column (least to greatest or greatest to least).

ACTIVITY 2 Cross Number Puzzle: LEVEL 3

Guided Conversation

If you think your students have mastered the ideas in Levels 1 and 2, you may want to push their thinking a little more in Level 3. If they haven't yet mastered the idea of the organized chart, practice that before moving on to this level.

Start out working as a whole class. Display the chart below with only the headings and the left-hand column filled in. Then invite students to share the results they gathered in Level 1 to help you complete the chart.

Numbers Used	Middle Numbers in the Puzzle Solutions	Sums of Both Rows
1 2 3 4 5	1 3 5	8 9 10
2 3 4 5 6	2 4 6	11 12 13
3 4 5 6 7	3 5 7	14 15 16
4 5 6 7 8	4 6 8	17 18 19

Use the information in the chart and the discussion questions on page 26 to help students start looking for patterns.

Behind the Math

As you develop the chart, allow plenty of time for students to share their thinking. If a student thinks she sees a pattern in one set of numbers, ask her to test the theory with another set of numbers. We're trying to build good observation and thinking skills, but we also need to make students understand that they always need to test their hypotheses. During these class discussions you'll notice how often your students are using math terminology and previously learned skills. Whenever you have the opportunity, ask them to explain their thinking. All of this helps build strong math thinkers.

Guided Conversation *continued*

Refer to the chart you've developed. Ask students:

- *Do you notice a pattern between the five consecutive numbers you used and the numbers that ended up in the middle box of the puzzle solution?*

- *Is it possible to predict the numbers in the middle box of the puzzle for any five consecutive numbers?*

Let's test that prediction. Suppose the numbers you are using in the puzzle are 10, 11, 12, 13, and 14.

- *What do you predict the middle numbers will be?*

- *Is it possible to predict the numbers in the middle if only the smallest of five consecutive numbers is given?*

- *If the smallest of the five consecutive numbers is 19, what are the numbers in the middle of the three puzzle solutions?*

- *If we know that the middle numbers are 15, 17, and 19, what five numbers were used?*

Next, you'll substitute a letter, *n*, for a number. Say to students, "*Let's call the smallest number used* n."

- *How can you find the numbers in the middle of the puzzle solution? Give your answers in terms of n.*

If students seem nervous about using a letter to stand in for a number, back up and review the answers they've already given. Lead them to see that for every set of five consecutive numbers, the numbers in the middle of the solution are the smallest number, the smallest number + 2, and the smallest number + 4. Plug in "*n*" for the smallest number and you have n, $n + 2$, and $n + 4$.

- *What if the smallest of the middle numbers is 99? What are the five numbers?* (As needed, point out that even large numbers follow the same pattern: n, $n + 2$, $n + 4$.)

Behind the Math

The number in the middle box is always the first, middle, or last number in the series of consecutive numbers.

For the set 10, 11, 12, 13, 14, the middle numbers will be 10, 12, and 14.

When the smallest number is 19, the set will be 19, 20, 21, 22, and 23. The middle numbers will be 19, 21, and 23.

If the middle numbers are 15, 17, and 19, the number set is 15, 16, 17, 18, and 19.

When we let *n* represent the smallest number, the middle numbers will be n, $n + 2$, and $n + 4$.

There's nothing mysterious about *n*—it just lets you write the pattern that you've figured out so it's shorter and easier to understand than if you wrote out "the smallest number" every time.

The three middle numbers are 99, 101, and 103. Hence, the five numbers used are 99, 100, 101, 102, and 103.

Guided Conversation *continued*

Tell students it's time to look for patterns in the sums. Point at the chart you developed at the start of Level 3. Ask:

- ***How are the sums of the horizontal and vertical boxes in each puzzle related?*** (As needed, point out that students should be looking at the three numbers in each box of the last column.)

Circle the middle number of each set of five—in other words, in the set 1 to 5, circle 3; in the set 2 to 6, circle 4, and so forth. Ask:

- ***How is the middle number in the set related to the middle number in the sums?*** (You may want to circle the middle number in each set in the far right column, as well.)

- ***What are the possible sums for puzzle solutions when we use numbers 5, 6, 7, 8, and 9?***

- ***What if we use numbers 99, 100, 101, 102, and 103?*** (Guide students to recognize that if they understand the pattern, then they can apply it to any set of five consecutive numbers, no matter how large.)

- ***When the smallest of the five consecutive numbers is 19, what are the possible sums?***

Now, let students substitute the letter *n* for a number.

- ***When the smallest of the five consecutive numbers used is*** n, ***what are the possible sums in terms of*** n? (Give students time to wrestle with this. Remind them that they know how to find the numbers; they just have to say it in terms of *n*.)

When a few students have figured it out, walk everyone through the answer in case some had trouble reaching it on their own. Then ask:

- ***What if we know that the sums are 26, 27, and 28? What are the five numbers used?***

Behind the Math

For any set of five consecutive numbers, the three sums are consecutive numbers.

The middle sum is 3 times the middle number in the set of five (or 3 times the middle number in the middle column).

The sums for 5 to 9 are 20, 21, and 22.

For 99 to 103 the sums are 302, 303, and 304.

The five numbers would be 19, 20, 21, 22, and 23; the sums would be 62, 63, and 64.

The five numbers would be n, $n + 1$, $n + 2$, $n + 3$, and $n + 4$. The middle sum is 3 times the middle number, so the middle sum would be $3(n + 2)$. Since the sums are consecutive numbers, the two other sums would be 1 less than the middle sum, $3(n + 2) - 1$, and 1 more than the middle sum, $3(n + 2) + 1$.

For 26, 27, 28, the number set is 7, 8, 9, 10, 11. A quick way to get the answer is to divide the middle sum, 27, by 3 to get the middle number in the set, 9, and then find the other 4 numbers in the set by adding and subtracting 1 and 2.

Rules of the Road

- Use number cards 1 to 9 to find correct solutions to the cross-shaped addition puzzle.
- Each number card may be used only once in each solution.
- Sum of the three horizontal boxes must equal the sum of the three vertical boxes.
- Solutions that have the same sums are the same solution. Solutions with different sums are different solutions.
- Write your solutions in the boxes below.

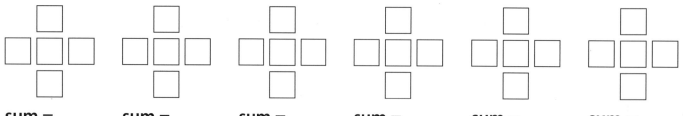

sum = _____   sum = _____   sum = _____   sum = _____   sum = _____   sum = _____

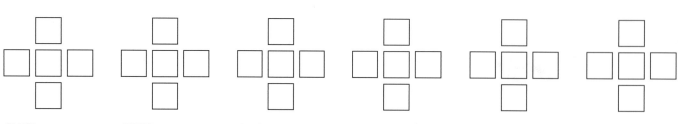

sum = _____   sum = _____   sum = _____   sum = _____   sum = _____   sum = _____

Every Child Can Do Math © Crystal Springs Books

ACTIVITY **3** Triangle Number Puzzle

Why Do This Activity?

Students will enjoy completing these puzzles, which provide plenty of practice on single-digit addition facts. But these simple-looking puzzles also encourage higher-order thinking. By creating organized lists of possible solutions for sets of 6 consecutive numbers, students see patterns emerge. These patterns give them the power to predict correct solutions for any set of 6 consecutive numbers. The same patterns can be used to start laying the foundations for algebra.

Prior Knowledge: addition facts to 30

Academic Vocabulary: sum, consecutive numbers

Rules of the Road

- Solve the puzzle by placing six number cards so that each side of the triangle adds up to the same sum.

- Each number card may be used only once in any puzzle solution.

Time: 15 minutes for Level 1; 20 minutes for Level 2; up to 30 minutes for Level 3

Materials & Preparation:

- 1 set of number cards 1–9 for each student (page 168)

- Number cards 10, 11, 12 for Level 3, for each student (make these by hand)

- Activity Sheet 3, 1 copy for each student (page 36)

- Document camera (optional)

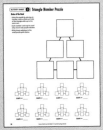

Activity Sheet **3**

Guided Conversation

It is helpful to complete Activity 2 with students before beginning Activity 3.

Give each student a set of number cards 1 to 9 and a copy of Activity Sheet 3. Instruct students to arrange cards in the blank boxes on Activity Sheet 3 so that the sum of the three numbers is the same on each side of the triangle. They may use any six number cards from the set of 1 to 9 to solve the puzzle.

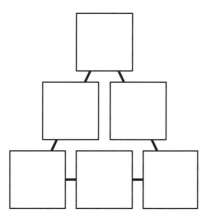

Give students ample time to find solutions. Ask them to record the solutions they find at the bottom of the activity sheet so you can refer to them later.

When each student has found at least one solution, invite some students to share their results. Record the six numbers they used and the sum for the solution. After writing down a few of these where everyone can see them, point to one solution and ask:

- *Did anyone come up with a solution that has a different sum, using these same six numbers?*

Encourage students to discuss the different approaches they may be using. Ask:

- *How do you go about finding solutions to the puzzles?*

- *What strategies are you using?* (You may notice at this point that some students are using guess-and-check, while others may have started a list similar to the ones used in Activity 2, Levels 2 and 3.)

Behind the Math

With a set of nine numbers and no restrictions, this puzzle has many solutions. Here are two examples:

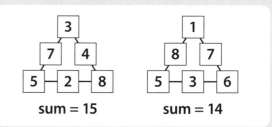

The same six numbers may or may not have more than one solution sum. One set of six that has two solution sums is shown below:

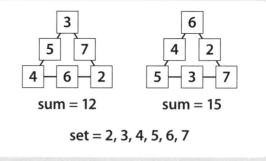

Two different sets of number cards also can give you a solution with the same sum.

Those at the guess-and-check stage are definitely getting practice with their number facts and may also be developing some number sense. They may not yet have an understanding of the relationships among the different combinations of numbers.

Guided Conversation

Now it's time to restrict the numbers that can be used. Tell students to use only cards 1 to 6. You want them to find all the combinations of three numbers that add up to 9, using just these six consecutive numbers. Say:

- *Rather than using guess-and-check to find the solutions, we're going to find all the possible combinations before we even put them into the puzzle.*

Set up an organized list where students can see it. Point out that, since this is an organized list, you're going to list the six numbers in order down the side of the chart. Then ask:

- *What combinations of three numbers add up to 9, for each of the numbers in the list?* (Stop filling in the chart when combinations start repeating, regardless of the order of the numbers.)

6	
5	
4	
3	
2	
1	

Now display the image of the triangle puzzle so students can see the completed number chart and the grid at the same time. Direct their attention to the empty boxes on the points of the triangle grid. Ask:

- *Which of the numbers, 1, 2, 3, 4, 5, or 6, CANNOT go in the corner squares?* (Give ample time for all students to think through this question before going on to the next.)

- *How do you know?*

Behind the Math

Fill in the combinations together with the students. It's helpful to start with the largest number first, which is why the list is organized that way. Say:

- *Let's look at 6. What other two numbers on this list, plus 6, have a sum of 9? Are there any other sums using 6 that total 9?*

Continue in this manner, listing only unique combinations. There are no new combinations for 3, 2, or 1.

6 + 2 + 1
5 + 3 + 1
4 + 3 + 2
3 (no new combinations)
2 (no new combinations)
1 (no new combinations)

The numbers 4, 5, or 6 cannot go in the corner squares. For a number to go into a corner square, it needs to be part of two different three-number combinations. The numbers 4, 5, and 6 each appear only once in the chart, so they can't go into corners.

"How do you know?" is an extremely important part of this discussion. Have several students explain their thinking, even if some are simply restating what others have said already. When students hear other students explaining how they did something, it is apt to have more impact than when we tell them something.

Guided Conversation *continued*

When students have completed the puzzle, ask:

- *Using the information from the chart, do you see how to complete the puzzle now?*

- *Can you find all possible solutions for other sums, using number cards 1 to 6?* (Encourage students to make organized lists and to decide what sum they are looking for before they begin each list. As needed, remind them that each number may be used only once in any combination, and each combination needs three numbers.)

Next, have students complete a list of possible puzzle combinations, this time using consecutive number cards 2 to 7. Give them a chance to work on their own. See if some notice that you need another piece of information. Ask:

- *What more do I need to give you before you can complete your list?*

Look at the chart with your students. Say you're going to see if you can draw any conclusions about what this total might be. Show your work as you talk through the answers to the following questions.

7
6
5
4
3
2

- *What's the largest sum you can get by adding three of the numbers from 2 to 7?*

- *Is there another combination of numbers on the list that will give you this same total? Why do you think that's true?*

- *What's the smallest sum of three numbers you can get from this list?*

- *Will any other three numbers on the list give you this same sum? How do you know?*

- *Even though these two sums won't work to solve the puzzle, what can we conclude about the sums that do solve the puzzle?*

Behind the Math

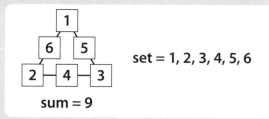

set = 1, 2, 3, 4, 5, 6

sum = 9

Using consecutive numbers 1 to 6, there are four possible solutions, with totals of 9, 10, 11, and 12.

You need to give them a target sum for the sides.

The largest possible sum is 18, found as (7 + 6 + 5). There is no other number combination that gives this sum because the rest of the numbers are too small to add up to 18.

The smallest possible sum is 9, found as (2 + 3 + 4). There is no other combination with this sum because the rest of the numbers are too large to add up to 9.

Possible sums that solve the puzzle fall between 9 and 18, but 9 and 18 are not possible solution sums.

Guided Conversation *continued*

Point out that that it's helpful knowing that the sums that solve the puzzle fall between 9 and 18, but we need to narrow the choices a bit more. What's a good way to do that? Remind students that to fill the triangle, they need three combinations with the same sum (one combination for each side of the triangle). You've already tried the extremes—the smallest and largest possible sums. These extremes each have only 1 combination, so they don't work. Try other combinations instead. Ask:

- *What sums should we try for next?*

After completing a list as a class for the suggested sum, have students work on their own, in pairs, or in small groups to find other sums using combinations of the numbers 2 to 7 that solve the puzzle. As needed, remind students to use organized lists.

Behind the Math

You may choose to try other possible sums in order, starting with 10 or 17, but if someone suggests that you try a sum from the middle of the range of 9 to 18, go with it.

Solution sums for 2 to 7 are 12, 13, 14, and 15.

ACTIVITY 3 Triangle Number Puzzle: LEVEL 3

Guided Conversation

In Level 3, you'll help students discover a pattern for finding the smallest and largest sums that solve the puzzle for any set of six consecutive numbers. Hand out the number cards for 10, 11, and 12 that you made to extend student sets. Divide students into small groups and assign each group one of the following sets of consecutive numbers:

3 to 8	5 to 10
4 to 9	6 to 11

(If you do not have the results from Levels 1 and 2 for the number sets 1 to 6 and 2 to 7, assign these sets as well.)

Ask each group to use organized lists to find the smallest possible sums for the sides of the triangle, using their number set. When they have finished that task, ask them to find the largest possible sum, using that same set. Allow time for each group to find the smallest and largest sum for their number set.

Behind the Math

Expect the discussion in Level 3 to take a lot of time, but it will be time well spent. It is important to allow students to discover the patterns and relationships among the numbers themselves. When they think they see a pattern, have them test it on other number sets, rather than simply accepting that it applies without testing.

Guided Conversation *continued*

Display or draw the following chart where all can see it. Complete the chart with your students by filling in each group's results as they find them.

Number Set	Smallest Puzzle Solution Sum
1 2 3 4 5 6	
2 3 4 5 6 7	
3 4 5 6 7 8	
4 5 6 7 8 9	
5 6 7 8 9 10	
6 7 8 9 10 11	

Once the chart is completed, call everyone together for a class discussion. Ask students:

- *Looking at the chart, is there a pattern? Look for a relationship between the six consecutive numbers in the set and the smallest possible sum.* (Don't move on until the class has agreed on a correct theory for relating the numbers in a set to the smallest solution sum for that set.)

Once they have a correct theory, it's time to test it some more. You want them to discover if they can apply what they've just learned to other sets of numbers. Ask:

- *Can you predict the smallest sum if the six consecutive numbers are 7, 8, 9, 10, 11, and 12? How did you find it?*

- *What would be the smallest sum if the six consecutive numbers are 71, 72, 73, 74, 75, and 76? How did you find it?*

Point out that a set of six consecutive numbers may be expressed algebraically as the numbers n, $n + 1$, $n + 2$, $n + 3$, $n + 4$, and $n + 5$. Ask:

- *What is the smallest possible sum using consecutive numbers n, n + 1, n + 2, n + 3, n + 4, and n + 5?* (This jump to algebraic symbols may be too much for some students, but others may be ready.)

Behind the Math

Number Set	Smallest Puzzle Solution Sum	Largest Puzzle Solution Sum*
1 2 3 4 5 6	9	12
2 3 4 5 6 7	12	15
3 4 5 6 7 8	15	18
4 5 6 7 8 9	18	21
5 6 7 8 9 10	21	24
6 7 8 9 10 11	24	27

* Largest solution sums are discussed on page 35.

The pattern you want them to find is that the smallest solution sum is 3 times the third number in the set of six consecutive numbers. Another correct pattern is that the smallest sum equals the sum of the second, third, and fourth numbers in the list.

The smallest sum for the set 7, 8, 9, 10, 11, 12 is 27, found as (3×9). Another way to find it is $(8 + 9 + 10)$.

The smallest sum for the set 71, 72, 73, 74, 75, 76 is 219, found as (3×73) or $(72 + 73 + 74)$.

For the set n, $n + 1$, $n + 2$, $n + 3$, $n + 4$, $n + 5$, the smallest solution sum is $3n + 6$. You may want to walk students through two ways to find the solution: Multiply the third number by 3 to get $3(n + 2)$. Using the distributive property, multiply both n and 2 by 3 to get $3n + 6$. Another approach is to add the second, third, and fourth numbers in the list: $(n + 1) + (n + 2) + (n + 3)$. When you add up the n's and the numbers, this statement also simplifies to $3n + 6$.

Guided Conversation *continued*

Add a column to your chart and have students look for the largest possible total for each number set. Ask:

- *Do you see a relationship between the six consecutive numbers in a set and the largest sum that works in the puzzle?*

End the activity as it began, by using the triangle number puzzle and number cards 1 to 9. But this time, ask:

- *What are the smallest and largest possible sums for the sides of the triangle using any six numbers from 1 to 9?*

(Give students time to find the solutions. Draw out the solutions as students give them to you until the smallest and largest sums are found.)

- *Are the numbers in each of these solutions consecutive numbers?*
- *Where are these numbers in relationship to the original set of 1 to 9?*

(It helps to list out numbers 1 to 9 horizontally. Ask students to point out the six-number sets that give the smallest and largest totals.)

Point to the puzzles on display, and ask students to think about the placement of the numbers in each puzzle. Ask:

- *For a given set of six consecutive numbers, what do you notice about where the numbers appear in the puzzle when the sum is the smallest possible?*
- *What do you notice with the largest possible sum?*

The largest sums are shown as the last column in the chart on page 34. The largest sum that solves the puzzle is 3 times the fourth number in the series of six consecutive numbers. Another way that works is to find the sum of the first, fifth, and sixth numbers.

For numbers 1 to 9, the smallest sum is 9 and the largest is 21.

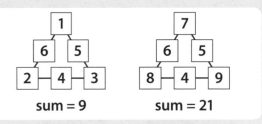

Yes, the smallest sum comes from numbers 1 to 6, which have the smallest values. The largest sum is from numbers 4 to 9, which have the largest values.

To get the smallest sum for a set of six consecutive numbers, the 3 smallest numbers need to be at the corners of the puzzle. To get the largest total, the 3 largest numbers need to be at the corners of the triangle puzzle. (You may use the word *vertices* instead of *corners* if your students have learned this term.)

Triangle Number Puzzle

Rules of the Road

- Solve the puzzle by placing six number cards so that each side of the triangle adds up to the same sum.

- Each number card may be used only once in any puzzle solution.

- Write down solutions in the small puzzle grids below.

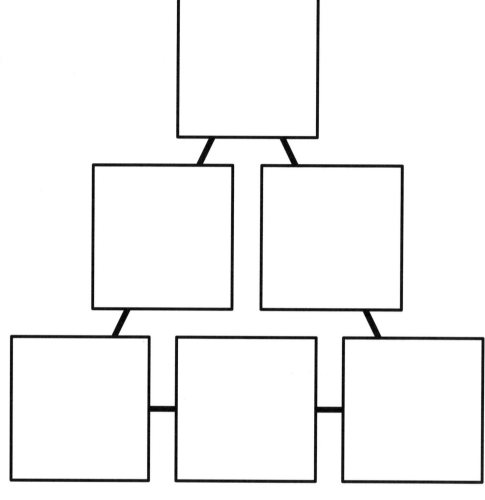

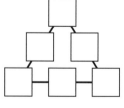

sum = _____

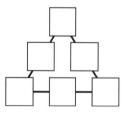

sum = _____

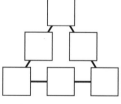

sum = _____

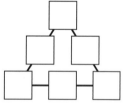

sum = _____

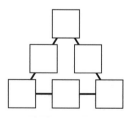

sum = _____

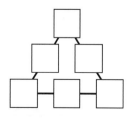

sum = _____

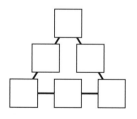

sum = _____

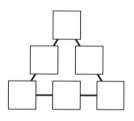

sum = _____

Every Child Can Do Math © Crystal Springs Books

ACTIVITY 4 Square Number Puzzle

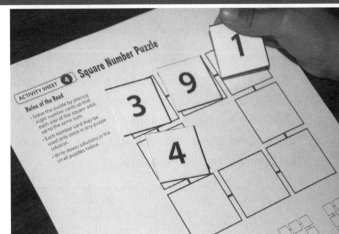

Why Do This Activity?

Level 1 of Activity 4 takes the puzzles from Activities 2 and 3 further by requiring students to find 4 solutions with the same sum, using a set of number cards. While doing so, students solidify their addition number facts for 1 to 9. Levels 2 and 3 give students the opportunity to further develop and apply the problem-solving skills and patterns of thinking used in Activities 2 and 3.

Prior Knowledge: addition facts to 20

Academic Vocabulary: sum, addends, consecutive numbers

Rules of the Road

- Solve the puzzle by placing eight number cards so that each side of the square adds up to the same sum.

- Each number card may be used only once in any puzzle solution.

Time: 15–20 minutes for Levels 1 and 2; up to 30 minutes for Level 3

Materials & Preparation:

- 1 set of number cards 1–9 for each student (page 168)

- Activity Sheet 4, 1 copy for each student (page 42)

- Document camera (optional)

Activity Sheet **4**

Guided Conversation

Activity 4 builds on the thought processes developed in Activities 2 and 3, so it is helpful to complete one or both of those activities with students before beginning Activity 4.

Give each student a set of number cards 1 to 9 and a copy of Activity Sheet 4. Tell students to use the cards on the puzzle grid to find combinations of the numbers 1 to 9 that will add up to the same sum on all 4 sides of the square puzzle. Have them record solutions on the sheet, along with the sum for that solution.

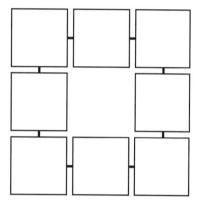

After giving your class plenty of time to work out various solutions, ask:

- **Can you come up with more than one solution using the same eight cards?** (In other words, is there more than one sum that works for all four sides, using the same eight cards?)

- **Can you come up with the same sum using 2 different sets of cards?** (For students who remember Activity 3, you may need to point out that you did not say they have to use consecutive numbers.)

As students work through these questions, record their answers so everyone can see solutions others have found. If you completed Activities 2 and 3, look to see whether anyone is using an organized list or another system to find all possible sums.

Behind the Math

With the freedom to choose any eight cards from 1 to 9, there are several number sets that can be arranged to get different solutions.

Here is an example set: 1, 2, 3, 4, 5, 6, 7, 9.

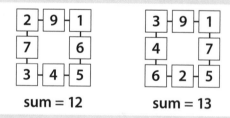

More than one set of numbers can give the same solution. Each set in this example differs by one number.

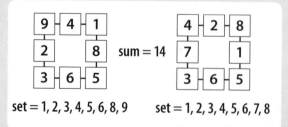

Guided Conversation

In Level 2, the focus of the puzzle narrows in order to encourage students to use an organized approach to solving it. Start by asking:

- *What is the greatest possible sum of any three of these cards, using cards 1 to 9?*

- *What is the least possible sum?*

Remind students that in order to complete the square puzzle, they have to find four different combinations of three numbers that have the same sum. Consider the greatest sum, 24. Ask:

- *For numbers 1 to 9, how many combinations of three numbers add up to 24?*

- *How many add up to the least sum, 6?*

- *Can you find a puzzle solution that adds up to the greatest or least sums possible for numbers 1 to 9?*

- *Can you find a puzzle solution using the greatest or least sums for any other set of consecutive numbers? Explain your thinking.*

Tell students that you could move on to testing the next-to-least or next-to-greatest possible sum. But taking this approach, you'll have 17 more possible totals to check. Not all of those sums are likely to have four different three-number combinations that work. Ask:

- *What sum should we test first, to save time?*

Tell students that you can save even more time by first finding all the sums that add up to this middle sum, 15. As a class, create a chart with the numbers 9 to 1 down the left-hand column. Starting with the largest number first, write all the combinations that use that number and 2 other numbers on the list and whose sum is 15. Leave out any repeats—that is, any "new" combination that uses the same three numbers as another, but in a different order. Ask students to complete the chart after you've done 1 or 2 rows together.

Behind the Math

The greatest possible sum is 24, which is the sum of the three largest numbers ($7 + 8 + 9$). The smallest possible sum is 6, the sum of the three smallest numbers ($1 + 2 + 3$).

For any set of numbers, there is only one set of three that has the greatest sum and only 1 set with the least sum. Since you need four combinations of numbers, the puzzle cannot be solved using the greatest or least sum as the solution. This will be true for all sets of consecutive numbers because no other numbers can have a value greater than the three largest or smaller than the three smallest.

Students already know that, for numbers 1 to 9, the range of possible sums is 6 to 24. They also know that neither 6 nor 24 work. Since the extremes don't work, it makes sense to try something from the middle of the range, such as 15.

Sums to 15

9	9 + 5 + 1	9 + 4 + 2	
8	8 + 6 + 1	8 + 5 + 2	8 + 4 + 3
7	7 + 6 + 2	7 + 5 + 3	
6	6 + 5 + 4		
5			
4			
3			
2			
1			

Guided Conversation *continued*

After students have completed the chart, ask them to use the 1 to 9 number cards to fill in the square puzzle with four combinations from this chart. Have them write their solutions on their activity sheets.

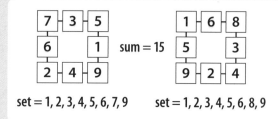
ACTIVITY ④ Square Number Puzzle: LEVEL 3

Guided Conversation

In Level 3, students look at questions similar to those in Level 2, but from different perspectives.

Have students create an organized list of all the combinations of three numbers from 1 to 9 that add up to 17. Work as a class or have students work alone.

Remind students that, even though it takes a while to make the list, it's still faster than doing guess-and-check. Plus, it may turn out that there are no solutions, which you'll never know if you use guess-and-check. You'd just keep trying, thinking that you hadn't found one yet.

When the list is complete, have students look at the digits in the different combinations. Ask:

- *Do any numbers appear in only one combination?*
- *Which position must this number go into, in the puzzle? How do you know?*

Point out combinations that contain the number 9. Ask:

- *What do you notice about the other 2 numbers in those combinations?*

Behind the Math

Sums to 17

9	9 + 7 + 1	9 + 6 + 2	9 + 5 + 3
8	8 + 7 + 2	8 + 6 + 3	8 + 5 + 4
7	7 + 6 + 4		

Note: For the set 1 to 9, there are no three-number combinations that total 17 that do not include 7, 8, or 9.

The number 1 appears in only one combination. It must go into one of the middle squares. It can't occupy a corner square because it is not in any other combination.

The other two numbers that go with 9 add up to 8.

Guided Conversation *continued*

Once students understand this pattern, ask them to tell you if it works for combinations with the number 8. Ask:

- *What do the other 2 numbers that go with 8 add up to?*

- *What about the 2 numbers that go with 7?*

- *Can you describe this rule in words?* (Students may phrase the rule a number of ways. Accept any wording that works.)

- *Do you think this rule would hold true for other puzzle solutions? Why do you think so?*

Ask students to find 4 combinations from the Sums to 17 chart that work in the square puzzle.

Encourage students to broaden their thinking. If time allows, ask:

- *If you add 10 to each number in a puzzle, do you still have a correct puzzle solution?*

- *How does the new sum compare to the original sum?*

- *Would this work for any number being added to each of the addends? How will it affect the new totals?* (It's worth proving this, using some solutions that students have come up with. Even if students are convinced without proof, testing ideas is an important part of doing math and science.)

- *What if you multiply each number by 10? Will the puzzle still work?*

Behind the Math

For combinations with 8, the other two add up to 9.

For the combination with 7, the other two add up to 10.

The rule can be described as: "When you have two three-number sums, and one of the numbers is the same in both, then the other two numbers will add up to the same sum."

This rule holds true for any 2 puzzle sides that share a corner (and therefore have an addend in common). It has to—otherwise the sums would not be the same on those 2 sides.

Two possible combinations are shown:

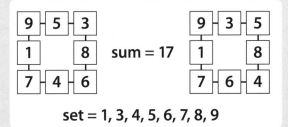

sum = 17

set = 1, 3, 4, 5, 6, 7, 8, 9

Yes, adding 10 to each addend gives you another puzzle solution. The sum for each side would be 30 more than the original sum. If you add any number to all the digits in the puzzle, then the new sum is the old sum plus 3 times the number you added. Develop the algebraic expression for students who are ready for it.

For $a + b + c = d$
$(a + x) + (b + x) + (c + x) = 3x + d$
Or, $3x + a + b + c = 3x + d$

Point out that, in the example you just did, $x = 10$, but it can equal any number.

Yes. If you multiply each number by 10, then the new sum will be 10 times the old sum.

Square Number Puzzle

Rules of the Road

- Solve the puzzle by placing eight number cards so that each side of the square adds up to the same sum.

- Each number card may be used only once in any puzzle solution.

- Write down solutions in the small puzzles below.

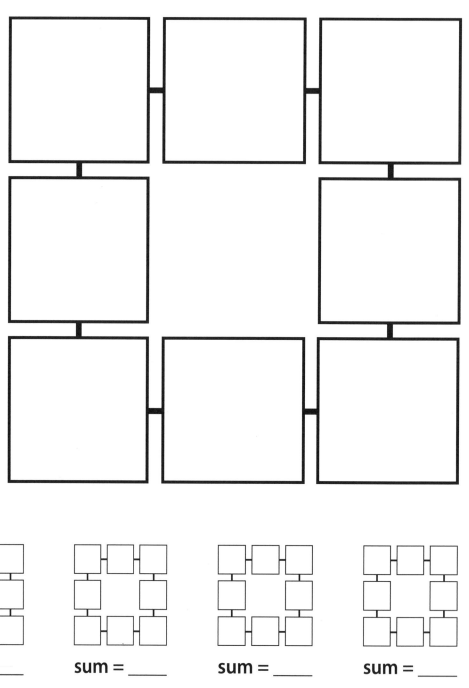

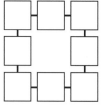
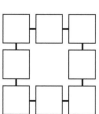

sum = _____   **sum = _____**   **sum = _____**   **sum = _____**   **sum = _____**

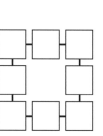
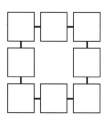
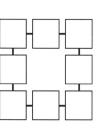
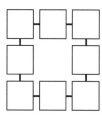
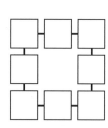
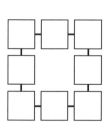

sum = _____   **sum = _____**   **sum = _____**   **sum = _____**   **sum = _____**

Every Child Can Do Math © Crystal Springs Books

ACTIVITY 5 Addition Sentences

Why Do This Activity?

This activity provides needed addition fact practice in a fun game. As students discover solutions to addition sentence puzzles, they think beyond basic facts and deepen their understanding of place value. Solving problems that have unique solutions, as well as those with multiple solutions, strengthens their understanding of equalities. Fluency in these facts and concepts frees students to think about math operations at a higher level, which lays a strong foundation for more advanced mathematics.

Prior Knowledge: addition facts, addition with and without regrouping, place value, number sentences and equality

Academic Vocabulary: digit, addends, sum, regrouping

Rules of the Road

- Use 0 to 9 number cards to find correct addition number sentence solutions.

- Use each card only once in each solution.

- No number may begin with 0.

Time: 10–15 minutes for Level 1; up to 20 additional minutes for both Levels 2 & 3

Materials & Preparation:

- 1 set of number cards 0–9 for each student (page 168)

- Activity Sheets 5A, 5B, and 5C, 1 copy of each for each student (pages 49–51)

- Document camera (optional)

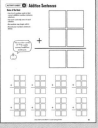

Activity Sheet **5A**

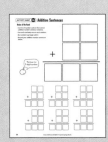

Activity Sheet **5B**

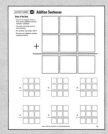

Activity Sheet **5C**

Guided Conversation

Show your class these two incomplete number sentences. Give students a moment to figure out solutions for each number sentence.

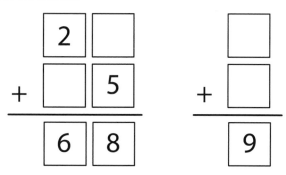

Invite students to share their answers, and then ask:

- *How do the solutions to these two number sentences differ?*

Give each student a copy of Activity Sheet 5A and a set of 0 to 9 number cards. Let them know whether you want them to work alone or in pairs.

Go over the Rules of the Road listed on the activity sheet. Explain to students that the game is played by placing number cards in the empty boxes to form a correct solution. Remind students that there may be more than one solution, as they saw in the example you just showed them.

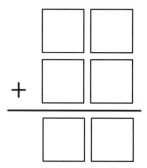

Give students plenty of time to come up with solutions. Walk around the room, monitoring progress and making sure everyone understands the task. Ask students to record any correct solutions they find in the grids at the bottom of Activity Sheet 5A.

Behind the Math

This warm-up will help prepare your students for the kind of thinking they'll use during the activity. The two-digit sentence has a unique solution ($23 + 45 = 68$), but the one-digit sentence can have a variety of solutions ($1 + 8 = 9; 2 + 7 = 9; 3 + 6 = 9; 4 + 5 = 9$). The same will be true of other number sentences in this activity. Some have only one solution, while others have multiple solutions.

Many correct solutions are possible.

Guided Conversation *continued*

After students have had a chance to tackle the puzzle, start a class discussion. Give students the opportunity to think about their answer to each question and to share the alternate approaches they used. The goal is to get all students thinking and sharing their thoughts and ideas, rather than moving on after one student gives a correct response.

- *Is there a number card you can't use?* (Check by asking students to raise their hands if they used the numbers 1, 2, 3, 4, 5, 6, 7, 8, and 9, calling out one number at a time.)

- *Did anyone use the number 0? Where did you use it?*

- *Do you think 0 can be used anywhere else? Why do you think that?*

As you ask the next set of questions, record the answers students give in a place where everyone can see them.

- *What's the largest sum you can make?* (Give students plenty of time to explore this challenge before asking the next two questions. Write down their suggested solutions.)

- *How many ways can you make this sum?*

- *How can you be sure it's the largest sum?*

Use the same approach to explore these questions as a class:

- *What's the smallest sum you can make?*

- *How many ways can you make this sum?*

- *How can you be sure it's the smallest?*

- *Is there an easy way to turn one solution into two solutions?*

Explore the answer to this question. Once students understand the solution, ask:

- *Why won't it work to swap digits from the ones place to the tens place?*

Behind the Math

All digits can be used. Zero, however, can be used only in the ones place in the sum. If students have trouble explaining why this is true, ask them to talk with a neighbor about the rules for the puzzle. They should realize that if 0 is used in the ones place of an addend, then the number in the other ones place wouldn't change, so they'd have to repeat that number in the sum, which is against the rules. Have students demonstrate this for themselves, using number cards.

The largest sum is 98. There are two ways to make it:

$$
\begin{array}{r} 56 \\ + 42 \\ \hline 98 \end{array}
\qquad
\begin{array}{r} 52 \\ + 46 \\ \hline 98 \end{array}
$$

One way to explain how you can be sure it's the largest sum is to point out that the only 2-digit number that's larger is 99, but since you can't use a digit twice in the puzzle, 99 doesn't work.

The smallest sum is 39. It can be made two ways:

$$
\begin{array}{r} 25 \\ + 14 \\ \hline 39 \end{array}
\qquad
\begin{array}{r} 24 \\ + 15 \\ \hline 39 \end{array}
$$

Students can be sure it's the smallest because the two digits with the least value (1 and 2) are used in the tens place. The next digit with the least value is in the tens place of the sum (3). The remaining two digits with the least value (4 and 5) are used in the ones place.

An easy way to find a second solution is to swap either the digits in the tens places, or the digits in the ones places.

Swapping between the ones place and tens place does not work because it changes the value of the number, which means that the sum changes.

Guided Conversation *continued*

Next, ask each student to choose any six cards and find a solution. Then ask:

- *Can you come up with another solution using these same six cards?*
- *What happens if you use a different set of six numbers?*

Have students save their completed Activity Sheets 5A for use in Activity 6.

Behind the Math

Yes, the same six digits can result in multiple number sentences. For example, the digits 1, 2, 4, and 7 can be used in the addends to create at least four different number sentences, as shown.

$$
\begin{array}{r} 42 \\ +\ 17 \\ \hline 59 \end{array}
\qquad
\begin{array}{r} 47 \\ +\ 12 \\ \hline 59 \end{array}
$$

$$
\begin{array}{r} 74 \\ +\ 21 \\ \hline 95 \end{array}
\qquad
\begin{array}{r} 71 \\ +\ 24 \\ \hline 95 \end{array}
$$

A different set of six numbers produces different results.

ACTIVITY 5 Addition Sentences: LEVEL 2

Guided Conversation

Give each student a copy of Activity Sheet 5B to use with their 0 to 9 number cards. Review the Rules of the Road. They are the same as in Level 1, but in Level 2 students are looking for solutions with 2-digit addends and 3-digit sums. When asking the questions below, allow plenty of time for students to look for an answer before you move on.

Point out that this time the sum is a 3-digit number. Ask:

- *Can you have a sum equal to 198? Why do you think so?* (Suggest that students place the digits for 198 in the sum of their sentence grid, and then work backward.)
- *What is the largest sum you can make?* (The next few questions will help guide students to the answer to this question. So you may want to move on to the next question without waiting as long as usual.)
- *What are the two largest digits you have to work with?*

Behind the Math

The sum cannot be 198. If students use the cards 1, 9, and 8 in the sum, then the remaining cards cannot add up to 198, no matter where they are placed in the addends.

The way to make the largest sum is to use the number cards with the greatest value, 8 and 9, in the tens place. In the tens place, they add up to 17 tens, or 170. So the largest value must start with 1 in the hundreds place and 7 in the tens place. (This is another reason why the sum can't equal 198—there are no two numbers that will add up to 19 tens, or 190.) The largest number remaining, 6, goes in the ones place. The numbers 4 and 2 add up to 6. The largest possible 3-digit sum is 176, which can be made two ways:

$$
\begin{array}{r} 94 \\ +\ 82 \\ \hline 176 \end{array}
\qquad
\begin{array}{r} 92 \\ +\ 84 \\ \hline 176 \end{array}
$$

Guided Conversation *continued*

- *Can you put the two largest number cards in the tens places of the two addends? What do they add up to?* (Remind students that 8 and 9 in the tens place add up to 17 tens, or 170—not 17. Have them place the 1 and 7 cards in the correct places in the sum.)

- *What is the largest number you have left? Can you use this in the ones place? Do you have numbers left that add up to this value in the ones place?*

- *How can you be sure that this is the largest sum?*

- *How many ways can you make this sum?*

- *What is the smallest sum you can make?*

- *How many ways can you make this sum?*

- *Does your neighbor have the same answer?*

- *Will 100 work as a sum? How about 101?*

Behind the Math

The smallest possible 3-digit sum is 102.

$$\begin{array}{r} 68 \\ + 34 \\ \hline 102 \end{array} \qquad \begin{array}{r} 64 \\ + 38 \\ \hline 102 \end{array}$$

The sums 100 and 101 won't work because they require repeating a digit.

ACTIVITY 5 Addition Sentences: LEVEL 3

Guided Conversation

Give each student a copy of Activity Sheet 5C to use with their 0 to 9 number cards. Remind students that the rules for the previous levels still apply.

Students should begin by laying out their cards to show two 3-digit addends, resulting in a 3-digit sum. They may write their solutions on the grids provided at the bottom of the activity sheet.

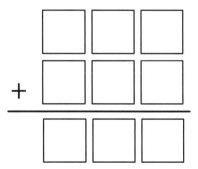

Behind the Math

Guided Conversation *continued*

When students have had enough time to investigate the puzzle, focus their attention on some specific questions. Ask:

- *If the sum in the number sentence is 981, does that mean you had to use regrouping? Explain your thinking.*

- *What are the possible addends for 981?*

- *Can you find a sum greater than 981?*

- *How many options do you have for where to place the 0? Can you explain why?*

- *Can the same set of digits be used to make different number sentences?*

Draw this grid where everyone can see it.

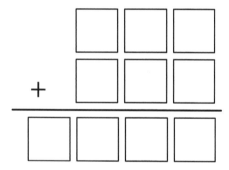

- *Can the sum be any 4-digit number? Why do you think so?*

Add 1 and 0 to the first two places in the 4-digit sum.

Ask:

- *How many solutions can you find?*
- *Does your neighbor have the same solution?*

- *Are there solution sums that don't have 0 in the hundreds place?*

Behind the Math

Yes, you have to regroup to get a 1 in the sum. The only way the sum of two digits can equal 1 is if the digits are 0 and 1 (which can't happen in this puzzle because you can't repeat a digit) or if the sum of the digits is 11, which requires regrouping.

Addends for 981 are $746 + 235$, $745 + 236$, and $735 + 246$. Remind students that they can swap digits of the same place value to find new addends. There is no sum greater than 981.

Zero can go only in 2 places—the ones place and the tens place of the sum. This is true because if 0 appeared in an addend, then a digit has to be repeated in the sum.

Yes, the same set of digits can provide more than one solution.

No, only 4-digit numbers that begin with 1 will work in the sum because the greatest value you can get by adding the greatest two single-digit numbers is a 2-digit number beginning in 1. Regrouping brings the 1 to the next highest place value, the thousands.

Here are 5 possible solutions:
$746 + 352 = 1098$
$764 + 325 = 1089$
$589 + 437 = 1026$
$764 + 289 = 1053$
$589 + 473 = 1062$

One sum with a digit other than 0 in the hundreds place is 1206 ($859 + 347$ and its variations).

Addition Sentences

Rules of the Road

- Use 0 to 9 number cards to find correct addition number sentence solutions.
- Use each card only once in each solution.
- No number may begin with 0.
- Record your number sentences below.

Use number cards 0–9 to make correct addition sentences.

$+$

Rules of the Road

- Use 0 to 9 number cards to find correct addition number sentence solutions.
- Use each card only once in each solution.
- No number may begin with 0.
- Record your addition number sentences below.

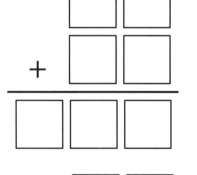

The sum is a 3-digit number.

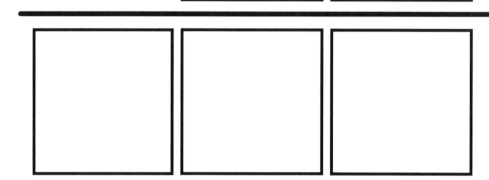

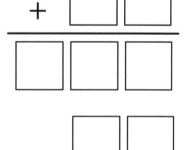

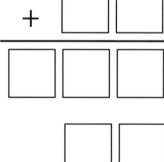

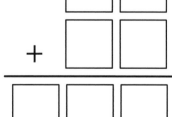

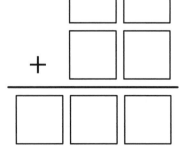

Addition Sentences

Rules of the Road

- Use 0 to 9 number cards to find correct addition number sentence solutions.
- Use each card only once in each solution.
- No number may begin with 0.
- Record your addition number sentences below.

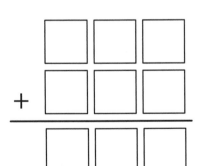

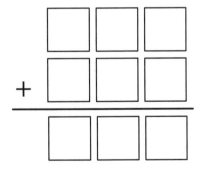

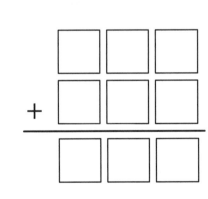

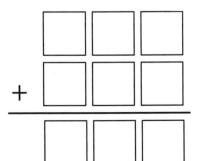

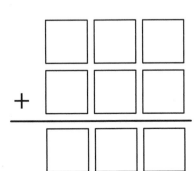

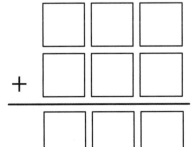

ACTIVITY ⑥ Subtraction Sentences

Why Do This Activity?

This activity gives students a fun opportunity to gain fluency in basic math facts and place value in the context of subtraction. Finding subtraction solutions by revisiting addition solutions helps students see that subtraction is the reverse of addition. This promotes flexibility with numbers and operations. Flexibility with numbers means that if students know that the sum of 5 and 3 is 8, then they also know that the difference between 8 and 3 is 5, and the difference between 8 and 5 is 3—so they know three times as many facts as they thought they did! Both fluency and flexibility contribute to creative thinking and solid problem-solving skills.

Prior Knowledge: subtraction facts, subtraction with and without regrouping, place value, and number sentences and equality

Academic Vocabulary: digit, minuend, subtrahend, difference, regrouping

Rules of the Road

- Use number cards 0 to 9 to find correct solutions to subtraction number sentence problems.

- No number card may be used more than once in each number sentence.

- No number in the sentence may begin with 0.

Time: 10–15 minutes for Level 1; up to 20 minutes each for Levels 2 & 3

Materials & Preparation:

- 1 set of number cards 0–9 for each student (page 168)

- Activity Sheets 6A, 6B, and 6C, 1 copy of each for each student (pages 58–60)

- Completed Activity Sheets 5A, 5B, and 5C (optional)

- Document camera (optional)

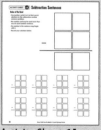

Activity Sheet **6A**

Activity Sheet **6B**

Activity Sheet **6C**

Guided Conversation

Begin the activity by giving the students a quick subtraction review to help focus their attention.

Set up the image below so the whole class can see it. Ask students to fill in the empty boxes to create a subtraction number sentence that is correct. Give them a minute to find the answer.

$$
\begin{array}{r}
5\ \square\ 4 \\
-\ 1\ 2\ \square \\
\hline
4\ 7\ 1
\end{array}
$$

Tell students that the problem they just solved was pretty straightforward because it has only one correct solution. Next, have students try this one, which requires a bit more thought:

$$
\begin{array}{r}
4\ \square\ 7\ 3 \\
-\ 1\ 6\ 2\ \square \\
\hline
\square\ 7\ 4\ 8
\end{array}
$$

There is still only one correct solution, but some regrouping is needed. Ask students:

- *What does the term* regrouping *mean?* (Encourage students to describe the process if they have difficulty defining it. Providing manipulatives may help them explain their answers.)

- *How can you tell that this problem requires regrouping?*

Behind the Math

$$
\begin{array}{r}
5\ \boxed{9}\ 4 \\
-\ 1\ 2\ \boxed{3} \\
\hline
4\ 7\ 1
\end{array}
$$

$$
\begin{array}{r}
4\ \boxed{3}\ 7\ 3 \\
-\ 1\ 6\ 2\ \boxed{5} \\
\hline
\boxed{2}\ 7\ 4\ 8
\end{array}
$$

Regrouping means to take a group from the next level of place value. In this case, it's impossible to subtract from the 3 in the units place and get 8, so regrouping must be taking place. Likewise, in the hundreds place, if 6 is subtracted and 7 is the result, then the number must have been 13, so again regrouping has occurred (from the thousands place to the hundreds place).

Guided Conversation *continued*

Give each student a copy of Activity Sheet 6A and a set of number cards 0 to 9. Let them know whether to work alone or in pairs. If you want to emphasize the vocabulary, you may want to review the terms *minuend, subtrahend,* and *difference* before using these terms during class discussions.

Go over the Rules of the Road listed on the activity sheet. Remind students that there may be more than one solution. Have them record answers in the grids at the bottom of the sheet. Give students plenty of time to come up with solutions. Walk around the room, monitoring progress and making sure everyone understands the task.

Give everyone a good amount of time to tackle the puzzle, and then direct the class's attention to the front of the room. Ask students to share solutions they found. Write these where everyone can see them. As you record solutions, ask the following questions. Give all students a chance to think about each question.

- *Can 0 go in any blank boxes? Which one? Explain your thinking.*

- *Why can't 0 go in the difference?*

- *Why can't 0 go in the subtrahend?* (Stay with a student who cannot explain her answer right away. Work with her until she can explain to the class the reasoning behind her answer. This develops the student's confidence in her own understanding.)

- *Can you find the number sentence with the greatest difference? Can you explain how you know you found it?* (Encourage students to use number cards to show how they determined that 97, not 98, is the greatest possible number that solves the puzzle.)

Behind the Math

The rules say that 0 can't be the first number, so it can't go in the tens place. In the ones place, 0 works only in the minuend.

Zero cannot be in the ones place of the difference because the same digit would have to be in the ones place of both the minuend and subtrahend. If 0 is in the ones place of the subtrahend, then the digits in the minuend and the difference would be the same. If 0 is in the ones place of the minuend, then you can regroup to subtract the number in the subtrahend. (Rather than repeating minuend and subtrahend, show students the placement of number cards on the grid whenever possible.)

To get the greatest difference, you want to start with the greatest 2-digit number and subtract the least 2-digit number.

$$\begin{array}{r} 97 \\ -\ 12 \\ \hline 85 \end{array}$$

The greatest number that works is 97 because 99 repeats a digit and because 98 requires 8 to be repeated in the difference.

Guided Conversation *continued*

- *Can you find the number sentence with the least difference? How can you convince your neighbor this is the least difference?* (Explaining *how* he found an answer is more important to developing the student's number sense than getting the right answer in the first place.)

Draw this addition problem for students, or use number cards to set it up where they can see it.

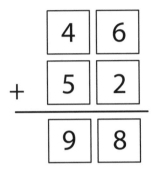

Ask:

- *Does this addition sentence help you come up with one subtraction sentence?*

- *Does it help you come up with two?*

If students completed Activity 5, Addition Sentences, have them take out Activity Sheet 5A. They can use the solutions they discovered in that activity to find more solutions for Activity Sheet 6A. If any student thinks that this shortcut is "cheating," reassure him that it is not. Addition and subtraction are reverse operations, and it's completely "fair" to use them that way. (Understanding reverse operations is also critical to developing strong number sense.)

Behind the Math

You want the difference to be the least possible 2-digit number. We know 10 won't work because you can't have 0 in the difference. Nor will 11 work because you repeat the 1. So that leaves 12. Any combination that gives you this difference will work.

Yes. Since subtraction is the reverse operation of addition, just turn this addition sentence into two subtraction sentences:

$$\begin{array}{r} 98 \\ -52 \\ \hline 46 \end{array} \qquad \begin{array}{r} 98 \\ -46 \\ \hline 52 \end{array}$$

Guided Conversation

Hand out copies of Activity Sheet 6B. Tell students to use any of their number cards 0 to 9 to make 3-digit subtraction sentences and record them at the bottom of the sheet. Tell students that they are free to use anything else they have available in order to find solutions. (This is a hint that it's okay to pull out Activity Sheet 5C, if students completed it.)

After everyone has had plenty of time to work, ask one student to come forward and record the differences from all the solutions students found so they are visible to all. (Students do not have to give minuends and subtrahends, just the differences.) There are many possible answers; it can be more manageable if the student who's recording first calls for all differences that fall between 100 and 199, then 200 and 299, and so on.

Ask the following questions after students have slowed down on sharing new differences:

- *What numbers will give you a difference of 123?*

- *Did anyone look back at their 3-digit addition sentences (Activity Sheet 5C)? How did those help you find solutions for the 3-digit subtraction sentences?*

Behind the Math

There are many possible solutions. Here are three:

$$\begin{array}{r} 890 \\ -\ 754 \\ \hline 136 \end{array} \qquad \begin{array}{r} 807 \\ -\ 593 \\ \hline 214 \end{array} \qquad \begin{array}{r} 970 \\ -\ 658 \\ \hline 312 \end{array}$$

One possible solution:

$$\begin{array}{r} 590 \\ -\ 467 \\ \hline 123 \end{array}$$

Other combinations will also give you this difference.

Students can subtract either of the addends from the sum in order to come up with a 3-digit subtraction sentence that works for this puzzle. For example:

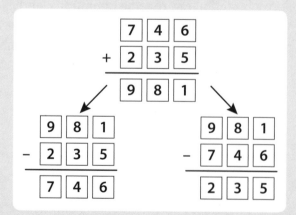

ACTIVITY ❻ Subtraction Sentences: LEVEL 3

Guided Conversation

Discuss the possible solutions for the following problem. Model the thinking students should practice. Ask:

- *If the difference is a single digit, what must be true of the digit in the tens place in both the minuend and the subtrahend?*

- *Since the two digits in the tens place can't start out the same, what must have happened in the computation to make them the same?*

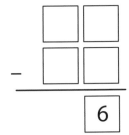

Next, ask students to consider the possible solutions for each of these two problems. (If some students get stuck on the first one, suggest they go on to the second before you discuss results of both as a class.)

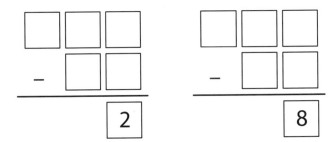

Hand out Activity Sheet 6C to students. Find the possible solutions for this subtraction number sentence. Point out that they will need to use all of their number cards 0 to 9. Have them record their solutions on Activity Sheet 6C.

After students have had a good amount of time to find different solutions, invite students to share their solutions. Then ask:

- *Does the number 1 have to be in any particular position? Explain your reasoning.*

Ask:

- *What numbers will give you a difference of 264?* (Regrouping will be required!)

Behind the Math

The digits in the tens place must be the same. But since they can't start out the same, regrouping must have changed the digit in the tens place of the minuend. There are numerous solutions if you can repeat digits. If you can use each digit only once, as in this activity, then there are far fewer solutions. Some examples:

$$
\begin{array}{r} 95 \\ -89 \\ \hline 6 \end{array}
\qquad
\begin{array}{r} 24 \\ -18 \\ \hline 6 \end{array}
\qquad
\begin{array}{r} 90 \\ -84 \\ \hline 6 \end{array}
$$

There is no solution to the first problem (difference of 2) using each number only once. Use number cards to show students why. Assuming the number card 2 is already used in the difference, the least 3-digit number we could use is 103, and the greatest 2-digit number we could use is 98. This difference is 5. Be sure to discuss *why* you know that there is no solution to the first problem. *Why* is more important than simply knowing that it has no solution.

The second problem has five solutions that all have a difference of 8.

$102 - 94 = 8$
$103 - 95 = 8$
$104 - 96 = 8$
$105 - 97 = 8$
$107 - 99 = 8$

Example solutions:
$1089 - 725 = 364$
$1098 - 756 = 342$
$1089 - 637 = 452$

The 1 card must be in the thousands place of the minuend. If any other number is used in this place, then the difference is a 4-digit number.

$1053 - 789 = 264$

Subtraction Sentences

Rules of the Road

- Use number cards 0 to 9 to find correct solutions to this subtraction number sentence problem.
- No number card may be used more than once in each number sentence.
- No number in the sentence may begin with 0.
- Record your solutions below.

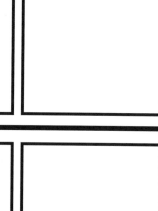

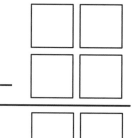

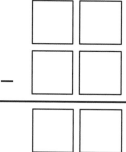

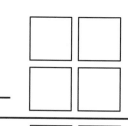

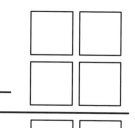

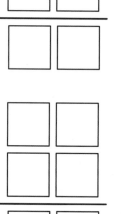

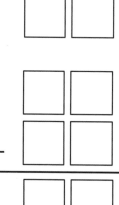

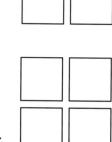

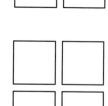

Every Child Can Do Math © Crystal Springs Books

Subtraction Sentences

Rules of the Road

- Use number cards 0 to 9 to find correct solutions to this subtraction number sentence problem.

- No number card may be used more than once in each number sentence.

- No number in the sentence may begin with 0.

- Record your solutions below.

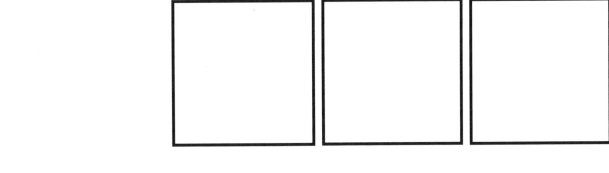

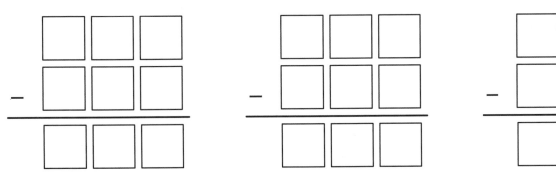

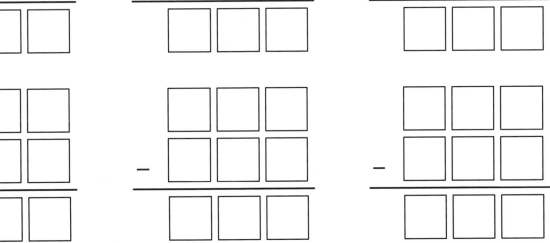

Subtraction Sentences

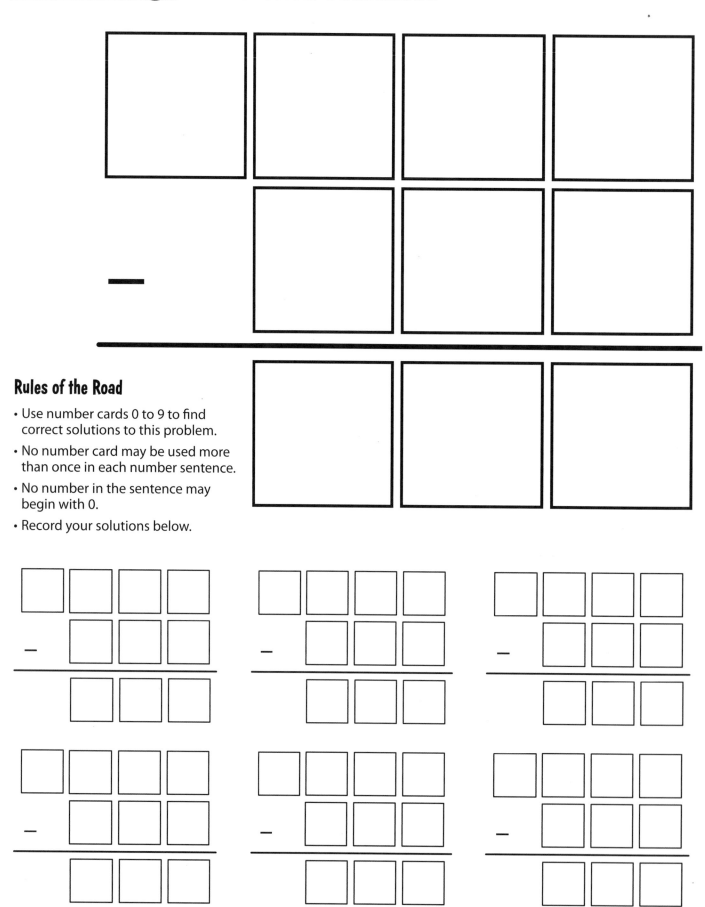

Rules of the Road

- Use number cards 0 to 9 to find correct solutions to this problem.
- No number card may be used more than once in each number sentence.
- No number in the sentence may begin with 0.
- Record your solutions below.

Every Child Can Do Math © Crystal Springs Books

ACTIVITY **7** Multiplication Sentences

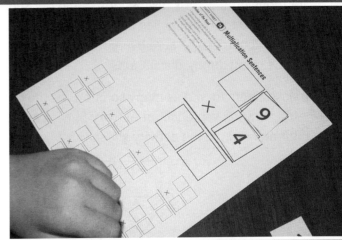

Why Do This Activity?

These number sentences give students opportunities to apply and practice their knowledge of basic addition and multiplication math facts and place value. Students work with problems that have unique solutions, as well as those with multiple solutions. This strengthens their understanding of equalities. Even students who struggle with math can do the Level 1 activities.

Prior Knowledge: multiplication facts, multiplication with and without regrouping, place value, number sentences and equality

Academic Vocabulary: product, factors, regrouping, multiplicand, multiplier, even and odd numbers

Rules of the Road

- Use number cards 0 to 9 to find correct solutions to multiplication number sentence problems.

- Each number card may be used only once in each number sentence.

- No number in the sentence may begin with 0.

Time: 10–15 minutes for Level 1; up to 20 additional minutes for both Levels 2 & 3

Materials & Preparation:

- 1 set of number cards 0 to 9 for each student (page 168)

- Activity Sheets 7A, 7B, and 7C, 1 copy of each for each student (pages 66–68)

- Document camera (optional)

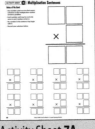

Activity Sheet **7A**

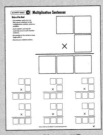

Activity Sheet **7B**

Activity Sheet **7C**

Guided Conversation

Set up the activity so you can use number cards to show solutions during class discussions. Hand out sets of number cards 0 to 9 and copies of Activity Sheet 7A. Review the vocabulary to be sure everyone knows the words you will be using during discussions.

Ask students to find as many solutions as they can to the multiplication sentence on Activity Sheet 7A and to record their answers on the activity sheet.

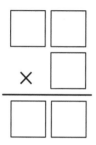

As always, allow students plenty of time to practice and think about what is happening. When all students have several solutions, start some good discussions to get them thinking through the math. Here are some questions to help get you started:

- ***Can you use the 0 card in any of the boxes?*** (Ask several students to explain what must be true of the factors for the 0 card to be in the ones place of the product. If they can't explain it, show several solutions and ask what they all have in common.)

- ***What is the least product you found?*** (As students share, write the products in a list where everyone can see them. Keep asking if anyone has a lesser product.)

- ***How can you be sure that you have found the least product?*** (Invite students to use number cards to demonstrate why this has to be the least product. Ask guiding questions to help students discover and explain why some other combinations do not work. It's worth the extra time you take to let students come to these conclusions on their own, rather than just telling them the answer.)

Behind the Math

There are many possible solutions to this number sentence. Encourage students to check each other's work if they want assurance that their solutions are correct.

Zero can be used only in the ones place in the product. It can be there only if the digit in the ones place of one factor is 2, 4, 6, or 8, and the digit in the ones place of the other factor is 5. These factors result in a product that ends in 0.

The least product is 52 (13 × 4).

The least product has to be a multiple of 13 because any multiple of 10 requires repeating the number 0 in the product; any multiple of 11 requires repeating a factor twice in the product (11 × 2 = 22, for example); and multiples of 12 require repeating the smaller factor in the product (12 × 3 = 36; 12 × 4 = 48; 12 × 5 = 60, but that's larger than 52.) Any multiple of 13 that's less than 13 × 4 requires repeating a digit.

Guided Conversation *continued*

- *What is the greatest product you can find? What factors give you this product?*

- *Can you find two other factors that give you this same greatest product? Do they work in this puzzle?*

Next, tell students to look at the solutions they wrote on their activity sheets. Ask:

- *Are some products odd and some even? How many odd products did you find? How many even products did you find?* (Keep track of the number of even and odd answers. You could create a class tally chart, comparing the number of even and odd products the class found. Or sharpen your class's mental math by keeping a running total. Go around the room from one student to the next, adding the new number to the previous total. For example: Ani says, "I found 3 even products, so the total is 3." Raul is next. He says, "I found 4 even products, so the new total is 7." Continue in this manner until the class has added all the even-number solutions. Then reverse the direction of students speaking and do the same process for finding the total number of odd-number products. See if they can pick up the speed!)

When all the evens and odds have been added, ask:

- *Why are there fewer odd products than even products?*

Behind the Math

The greatest product is 98. Either 49×2 or 14×7 will give you this product, but 49×2 requires repeating the 9 card so there is only one solution (14×7).

The products are both even and odd, but there will be more even answers than odd answers. This happens even though there are 5 odd digits to use in the factors and only 4 even digits (because 0 can't be part of the factors).

You will always have fewer odd products because only one combination of factors produces an odd product:

even $\times$ even $=$ even
even $\times$ odd $=$ even
odd $\times$ odd $=$ odd

Guided Conversation

Hand out Activity Sheet 7B (and sets of number cards 0 to 9, if you haven't already). Ask students to use the number cards to find and record solutions for the multiplication sentence on the activity sheet.

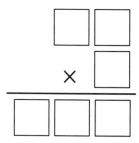

Remind them to record solutions at the bottom of the sheet.

After students have worked for a while, ask:

- *This is the product of a 2-digit number and a 1-digit number. What has to happen in order to get a 3-digit answer?* (Even if the first person gives you a correct answer, call on other students to explain their thinking. If they say they did it the same way as the previous person, tell them you'd still like to hear them describe the process they used. Sometimes they may restate it slightly differently, and that's a good thing because it helps other students to catch on to the concept. Plus, by pushing for them to share, it lets them know you really want to hear what *they* are thinking.)

Ask some of the following questions. Each time, allow several people to share their thinking.

- *Can 0 be a digit in either of the factors? How do you know?*

- *What is the least (smallest) product you can find?* (If students need help getting started, suggest that they start by determining what is the least 3-digit number and then considering if they can find factors to produce this number.)

Behind the Math

There are many possible solutions. Encourage students to check each other's work if they want assurance that their solutions are correct.

In order to have a product that is a 3-digit number, some regrouping has to occur.

Zero can't be used in either of the factors. If it were, then 0 would be needed in the product, and only one 0 card is available.

In solving these puzzles, it can be helpful to start out with guess-and-check, focusing on the final product you want. For example, when trying to find the least 3-digit answer, consider what the options are: 100, 101, 102 . . . As you look for factors that yield this product, you'll find the first one that works is $53 \times 2 = 106$. This is a more organized, systematic approach to finding the answer than random guessing.

Guided Conversation *continued*

- *What is the greatest product you can find?* (Again, suggest students think about the greatest number the product could be and consider possible factors for that product.)

Behind the Math

An approach similar to the one for finding the least product can be used for finding the greatest product, which is $95 \times 8 = 760$.

ACTIVITY ⑦ Multiplication Sentences: LEVEL 3

Guided Conversation

Hand out Activity Sheet 7C. Ask students to find and record solutions to this multiplication sentence:

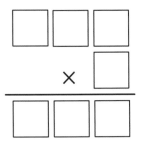

After students have had time to come up with a few solutions, ask the following questions:

- *Are there number cards that cannot be used in this problem? If so which ones, and why can't they be used?*

- *Are there any digits that can be used only in certain places?*

- *Is a product of 987 possible? If so, give its factors. If not, explain why.*

- *Is a product of 102 possible? If so, give its factors. If not, explain why.*

Behind the Math

All the number cards 0 to 9 can be used.

Zero can be used only in the tens place of the 3-digit factor and then only if regrouping was needed when multiplying the two digits in the ones place.

The product 987 is impossible. In order to get the 7 in the ones place, you would have to multiply 3×9 to get 27, but you already used number card 9 in the product.

No, this isn't possible because the only way to get a product of 102 is 102×1. That solution is against the rules of the game because it repeats the 1 and the 2.

Multiplication Sentences

Rules of the Road

- Use number cards 0 to 9 to find correct solutions to this multiplication number sentence problem.
- Each number card may be used only once in each number sentence.
- No number in the sentence may begin with 0.
- Record your solutions below.

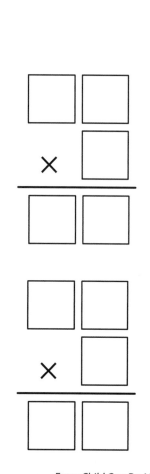

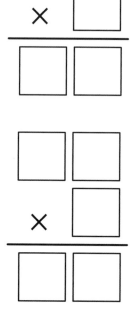

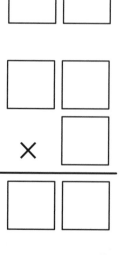

Every Child Can Do Math © Crystal Springs Books

Multiplication Sentences

Rules of the Road

- Use number cards 0 to 9 to find correct solutions to this multiplication number sentence problem.

- Each number card may be used only once in each number sentence.

- No number in the sentence may begin with 0.

- Record your solutions below.

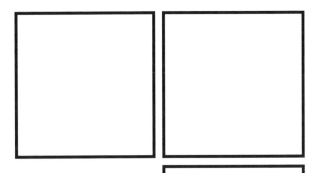

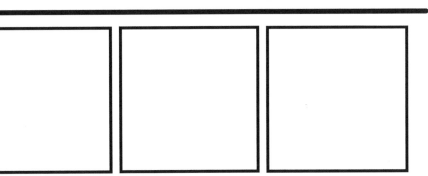

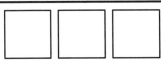

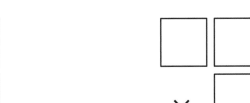

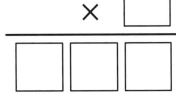

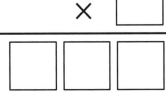

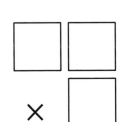

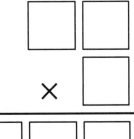

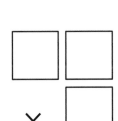

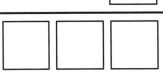

Multiplication Sentences

Rules of the Road

- Use number cards 0 to 9 to find correct solutions to this multiplication number sentence problem.
- Each number card may be used only once in each number sentence.
- No number in the sentence may begin with 0.
- Record your solutions below.

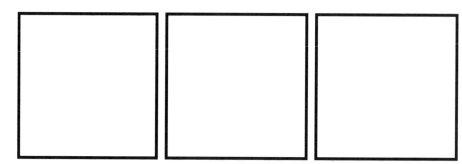

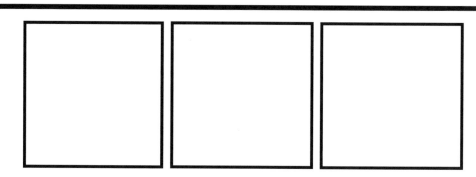
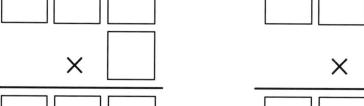
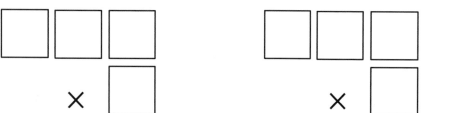
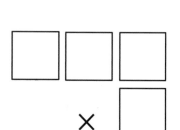
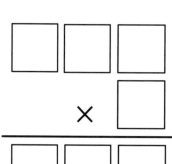
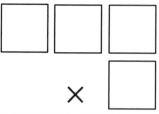

Every Child Can Do Math © Crystal Springs Books

ACTIVITY ⑧ Alternative Algorithms

Why Do This Activity?

This activity is rich with ideas for using alternative approaches to solve problems. These approaches give you terrific jumping-off places for classroom discussions. Discussions promote number sense because they involve higher-order thinking skills and richer understanding than if you just teach students an algorithm, procedure, or rule. Many students will understand these alternative approaches intuitively because they can connect them to something they already know and understand. Along the way, math is demystified, and numbers are recognized as something that students understand and can manage.

Prior Knowledge: basic computation skills

Rules of the Road

The goal of the discussions is to help students discover why these alternative approaches work. Some basic guidelines help to promote these kinds of discussions.

- Introduce only one or two examples at one time.

- Don't react immediately to any answer, right or wrong, that students suggest. Instead, have students test their ideas on other numbers to find out whether they're right or wrong.

- Give students plenty of time to think and to talk with each other about their ideas. The point is to think about why an answer is right, not to get the right answer.

- When a student suggests a new way of looking at a problem, discuss it as a class. Spend time testing the idea. Make sure students realize that there are many ways of thinking about numbers and therefore many ways to reach the right answer.

- Once most students have the right answer, take plenty of time to talk about why it is right. Have various students prove their answers are right, using multiple methods. This promotes flexibility in problem-solving.

- After introducing one or two new ways of thinking, refer back to these methods while solving similar problems in your math curriculum.

In no way do these discussion activities cover all the alternative routes people with good number sense may use. The hope is that getting your students to discuss these approaches will better equip them to come up with their own methods of solving problems in the future.

Time: 15 minutes for Level 1; up to 20 minutes each for Levels 2 & 3

Materials & Preparation:
- Board, screen, or other method of writing and displaying for a large group

Guided Conversation

It's time to introduce your class to Our Friend Yuki.

We call our friend Yuki (pronounced YOU-key). But you may want to have your class name this new friend, or you may simply call him or her "Our Friend."

Your students may have seen Our Friend Yuki on their activity sheets. Now it's time for you to put Our Friend to work in your classroom. Our Friend will help you have some rich math discussions with your students. He helps guide them to discover some techniques he likes to use to make solving math problems quicker and easier. Our Friend's methods also promote solid number sense.

Start out by telling your students that you have a friend (or new student) who's their age. Draw Our Friend for your students.

Tell students that Our Friend is very good at math. He's going to show them some ways that he likes to solve math problems. They need to be detectives and figure out how Our Friend is solving the problem.

Once Our Friend has been introduced and named, begin the discussions. Write 8 + 6 and 5 + 7 on the board, along with two empty thought bubbles for Our Friend. Say:

- *Our Friend sees 8 + 6 and 5 + 7 and thinks this: 10 + 4 and 10 + 2.* (Write Our Friend's thoughts in the two bubbles.)

8 + 6   5 + 7

Behind the Math

Spend a week or two practicing the alternative ways to think about addition and subtraction in Level 1. Do only one or two of the examples at a time. After introducing each one, refer back to the new methods as you solve similar problems in your regular curriculum. Once your students understand how flexible they can be in solving problems, move on to Level 2 to get them thinking about alternative ways to solve multiplication problems.

Keep Our Friend Yuki's drawing simple so you can draw him quickly. Chances are that when students get stuck on a problem in the future, they may ask Yuki to reappear to give them a hint!

Guided Conversation *continued*

Ask:

- **Why does Our Friend think this? What do these sums have to do with 8 + 6 and 5 + 7?** (Give students lots of time to discuss Our Friend's ideas. Ask questions to get them to explain their thinking. Let them give wrong answers at first, without letting on that they're wrong. Instead, ask them to prove their ideas. After a good discussion, draw the number bonds shown at right. Discuss why both approaches work. Spend time on this question until all students see what is happening. Then move on to the next question so they can apply what they've learned right away.)

- **What might Our Friend think when he sees 3 + 9?** (Again, allow plenty of time for class discussion. Encourage students to share their ideas by writing them on the board. Invite a student to draw a number bond to show where Our Friend's idea comes from.)

Draw the problem below, with Our Friend's face and an empty thought bubble next to it. Then ask:

- **What might Our Friend Yuki think when he sees 4 + 7 + 8 + 3 + 2? Why would he think this?** (Give students time to think about these questions and discuss possible answers as a class, then add Our Friend's idea (10 + 10 + 4 = 24) to his thought bubble.)

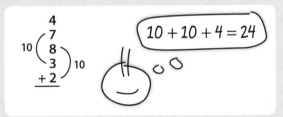

- **What would Our Friend do with this problem: 14 + 5 + 6 + 5 + 2?**

Behind the Math

Our Friend is making 10s from the numbers in the problem. He knows that 10s are important. Draw the number bonds that show why Our Friend's thinking works.

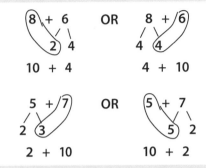

Be sure children see that, for each problem, both approaches work for forming 10s. It's important to stress flexibility in solving problems because flexibility is an important part of number sense.

When Our Friend sees 3 + 9 he might think 2 + 10.

Our Friend would look for combinations that make 10. He knows 10 and decades of 10 are easy to compute. He would see "4 + 7 + 8 + 3 + 2" as "(7 + 3) + (8 + 2) + 4," which is "10 + 10 + 4 = 24." Our Friend can do this in his head—and so can your students, once they get the hang of it.

Our Friend might be thinking:
14 + 6 = 20
5 + 5 = 10
So, 20 + 10 + 2 = 32

Guided Conversation *continued*

Tell students that Our Friend is thinking about 6 + 7. Draw Our Friend with his thoughts, shown below. Ask:

- *Can you figure out how Our Friend is thinking about the numbers this time?*

- *Did any of you think 12 + 1 when you saw this problem?* (If anyone did, ask them to explain their thinking to the rest of the class.)

$$6 + 7 = ?$$

$$12 + 1 = 13$$

- *What might Our Friend think when he sees 8 + 9?* (Take time to talk through options so that students recognize the multiple ways to think about this problem that make it easy to solve.)

Write 83 + 51 where students can see it. Tell them that this time, Our Friend Yuki has drawn something to help him think about the problem. Draw Yuki and his number line, as shown. Ask:

- *What is Our Friend using to help with this problem? How is he using it? How does this make the problem easier?*

$$83 + 51 = ?$$

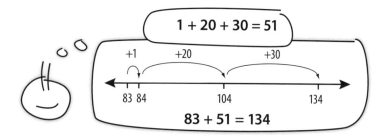

$$1 + 20 + 30 = 51$$

+1 +20 +30

83 84   104   134

$$83 + 51 = 134$$

Behind the Math

Our Friend knows he can look at the same problem in multiple ways. He might see 6 + 7 as 10 + 3 if he's thinking about making 10s, but this time he is thinking about making doubles. Our Friend knows that 6 + 6 is 12, so 6 + 7 is 12 + 1.

If Our Friend is still thinking of doubles, then he might see 8 + 9 and think, "8 doubled is 16, so 8 + 9 is 16 + 1." Or he may make 10s and turn 8 + 9 into 7 + 10. Both approaches work. Although these are simple sums, this kind of thinking applies to greater numbers and to other operations.

Our Friend is using an empty number line that he has drawn. In the first example, he's counting on from 83, making sure his "jumps" total 51.

Guided Conversation *continued*

Next, draw the subtraction problem 51 – 27 and Our Friend's thoughts. Then ask these questions:

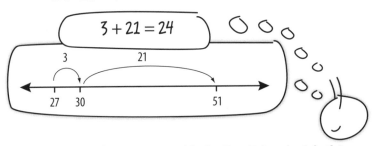

51 - 27 = ?

$3 + 21 = 24$

- *How does this same tool help Our Friend with this subtraction problem? How is Our Friend using it?*

- *Can Our Friend use the number line a different way to solve this subtraction problem? Why or why not?*

Tell students that, to solve 52 + 37, Our Friend is showing them another way to think about adding. Can they figure out what it is?

$50 + 30 = 80$

Easy!

52 + 37 = ?

$2 + 7 = 9$

Ask students:

- *How might Our Friend think about 46 + 82?*

Behind the Math

In this example, Our Friend is counting on again, even though this is a subtraction problem. Our Friend could have jumped backward from 51 to 27, but he finds adding easier than subtracting, and he knows that the difference between the two numbers is the same whether you count up or back.

This second example is similar to the way people in stores count back change if the cash register isn't able to calculate it for them. If someone buys something for 57 cents and gives the clerk a dollar, the clerk can hand back the change saying, "57, (hands over 3 pennies) 60, (hands over a dime and a nickel) 75, (hands over a quarter), and 1 dollar." Look at how that would appear on a number line:

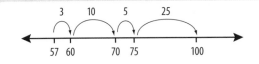

Change back from $1.00 for 57¢

Our Friend is adding place value amounts, starting at the left and moving to the right. In this problem he sees 52 + 37 as 5 tens and 3 tens (50 + 30) plus 2 ones and 7 ones (2 + 7), to get 8 tens (80) + 9 ones (9), or 89.

Our Friend might think, "46 + 82 is 4 tens and 8 tens (40 + 80) plus 6 ones and 2 ones (6 + 2), or 120 + 8 = 128"

Guided Conversation *continued*

Draw this next problem and ask students:

- **What is Our Friend doing here? How does it help make finding the difference easier?**

$16 - 7 = ?$

Same as 19 – 10

If students need a bit of help to figure out how changing the numbers makes things easier, ask them how difficult this problem is to solve:

$$\begin{array}{r} 52 \\ -10 \\ \hline 42 \end{array}$$

Easy!

Here's another approach to help students see what is happening here. Start with $8 - 3$ and rewrite it as $9 - 4$. Ask:

- **What did I do to both the 8 and the 3 to get the 9 and the 4?**

$$\begin{array}{r} 8 \\ -3 \\ \hline 5 \end{array} \rightarrow \begin{array}{r} 9 \\ -4 \\ \hline 5 \end{array} \rightarrow \begin{array}{r} 11 \\ -6 \\ \hline 5 \end{array} \rightarrow \begin{array}{r} 21 \\ -16 \\ \hline 5 \end{array} \rightarrow \begin{array}{r} 25 \\ -20 \\ \hline 5 \end{array}$$

Continue asking students what is happening to the two numbers in the problem as you move from one pair of numbers to the next in this series. Then ask:

- **What is happening to the difference in each of the problems? Why does this happen?**

This is such a great way for kids to overcome errors they may have been making in subtraction that it is worth spending plenty of time on this.

One more way to get this idea across involves a giant number line on the floor. You can easily make one with a black marker and wide masking tape. Have two students stand on two different numbers a certain distance apart. Ask them:

- **How far apart are you on the number line?**

Behind the Math

Our Friend is coming up with easier numbers to subtract by adding the same value to both of the numbers:

$16 + 3 = 19$
$7 + 3 = 10$

The difference between 16 and 7 will be the same as the difference between 19 and 10. Changing the numbers makes it easier because it's easier to subtract 10, compared with subtracting 7.

Oftentimes, students who have learned only a subtraction algorithm, without developing good number sense, apply the algorithm incorrectly and come up with 11 in answer to $16 - 7$. Practice Our Friend's method with many problems to get students to see that adding the same number to two numbers does not change the difference between the two numbers.

Adding 1 to both the 8 and the 3 gives you 9 and 4.

The difference stays the same because the same value is being added to both of the numbers in the problem.

Here is another way to explain this using the distributive property and negative numbers:
$$9 - 4 = (9 + 1) - (4 + 1)$$
$$= 9 + 1 - 4 - 1$$
$$= 9 - 4$$

This approach shows that you haven't really changed the problem.

Guided Conversation *continued*

- *Is that the same as saying that amount is the difference between your two numbers?*

- *I'd like each of you to jump two spaces to the right. What numbers are you standing on now? What is the difference between those two numbers? How does that compare to the difference between your original two numbers?*

Keep going in this manner until students see the connection to what Our Friend has done. You might even have them move to the left occasionally, which would prepare them for the next discussion activity.

Draw the next problem with Our Friend's thoughts alongside. Start the discussion with the questions below.

- *What has Our Friend done to make the numbers easier?*

- *But why is this easier? Before, Our Friend changed numbers to make them end in zero. This number already ends in 0. So why is he changing it? What's different about this situation?*

Behind the Math

Yes, how far apart the two students are is the same as the difference between their two numbers. As long as the students move the same number of spaces in the same direction, then their difference will be the same as it was originally.

Using the same ideas from the previous discussion activity, students should figure out that Our Friend has made the problem easier by *subtracting* 1 from both numbers in the problem, rather than adding. This subtraction compensation eliminates the need for regrouping. This might be a little harder for children to grasp than some other methods. In this problem Our Friend starts with the number 800 and decides to change it. Lead students to see that, by subtracting 1 from both numbers, we change the first number to 799 and eliminate the need for regrouping.

Keep in mind this is not a mathematical trick. You can show students the math behind what we are doing by using number bonds.

$$800 \quad - \quad 8$$
$$1 \quad 799 \qquad 7 \quad 1$$
$$(799 - 7) + (1 - 1) = 799 - 7$$

Some students may also understand this better if you say, "The original problem asks you to take 8 from 800. When I changed 800 to 799, I already took 1 away from the 800 so now I need to take away 7 more."

Guided Conversation

Show students Our Friend's thinking about the problem 29 × 4. Ask:

- *Where did Our Friend get 120? Did he multiply? What did he multiply?*
- *How come Our Friend is subtracting to solve a multiplication problem? How does that work?*

$$29 \times 4 = ?$$

120 − 4 = 116!

Write the problem shown below, and then tell students that Our Friend was going to do this problem on his calculator. But Our Friend discovered that the 9 button was broken. How did he do this problem on his calculator without using the 9 button?

$$\begin{array}{r} 1234 \\ \times \ \ 59 \\ \hline ? \end{array}$$

If students get stuck after you've given them plenty of time to think this through, tell them Our Friend wants to give them a hint.

Draw Yuki.

60

Ask:

- *What do you think Our Friend means by saying, "60"?*
- *How does he use 60?*
- *How can Our Friend find 59 groups of 1234 after finding 60 groups of 1234?* (As needed, point out that Our Friend is using a calculator for these problems. Yes, even Our Friend Yuki uses a calculator sometimes!)

Behind the Math

Our Friend got 120 by multiplying 30 by 4. Why would he do that? He knows that 29 × 4 can be thought of as 29 groups of 4. He knows 30 groups of 4 is 120 (30 × 4 = 120). But he also knows that he wants only 29 groups of 4, so he needs to take away (subtract) 1 group of 4 from that product. So, 120 − 4 gives him the answer to 29 × 4.

With practice, most students can do problems like 29 × 4 in their heads. There is no need to grind through the traditional algorithm of multiplying 9 and 4, writing down the 6 and "carrying" the 3, then multiplying 2 × 4 and adding 3. Yes, you can get the answer that way, but why do it? Our Friend's methods are faster, and they instill a deeper, stronger understanding of numbers.

Our Friend decides to change 1234 × 59 to 1234 × 60 so he doesn't need to use the 9 key:

$$1234 \times 60 = 74{,}040$$

Since Our Friend isn't really looking for the answer to 60 groups of 1234, he then subtracts 1234 from the product so he ends up with 59 groups:

$$74{,}040 - 1234 = 72{,}806$$

One of your students may take a different approach, such as saying, "Multiply 58 × 1234 and add another group of 1234 to that product." This is perfectly fine, and the fact that students see more than one way to solve the problem shows that they are developing good number sense. Encourage students to describe these multiplication problems as a certain number of groups of another number.

Guided Conversation continued

Tell students that Our Friend has another way to make multiplying easier. Ask them to figure out what he's doing. Talk students through the answer until they understand.

84×5 $840 \div 2$

Tell students that Our Friend has a third way to multiply. He understands how to find area, so when he saw 743×25, he drew an area diagram. Draw the problem and the diagram for students, and then discuss using the questions below.

$743 \times 25 = ?$

	700	40	3
20			
5			

- *Can you figure out what to put in the empty boxes in Our Friend's diagram?*

- *How does Our Friend's diagram help him find the answer to this multiplication problem?*

Behind the Math

Our Friend knows that 5 groups of 84 is the same as half of 10 groups of 84. Ten groups of 84 is easy—it's 840. Half of that is also easy—it's 420. So, 5 groups of 84 equals 420 (or $84 \times 5 = 420$). At first, it may seem wasteful to go through so many extra steps to reach an answer, but the time invested in helping students to understand this kind of thinking pays off. Once students can think flexibly about numbers, even problems involving large numbers become easy.

	700	40	3
20	14,000	800	60
5	3,500	200	15

$$17,500 + 1,000 + 75 = 18,575$$

Our Friend's diagram is an area model. It's an organized way to show all the partial products that make up the problem he is doing. The area model shows how to multiply factors using expanded notation. Expanded notation lets Our Friend multiply multiples of 10s, 100s, and so on, which is easier than multiplying digits. It also makes the problem very visual, and it's easier to keep track of the value of each digit (ones, tens, hundreds) in both factors.

When Our Friend adds all these partial products together, he will have the answer to the original problem ($743 \times 25 = 18,575$).

ACTIVITY 8 Alternative Algorithms: LEVEL 3

Guided Conversation

In Level 3, the alternatives to traditional algorithms use number properties that students may or may not have learned yet. But seeing the properties used in the context of Our Friend Yuki's solutions will give students an excellent foundation for making these properties their own, whenever these number properties are formally introduced.

Guided Conversation *continued*

Tell students that Our Friend sees the following problems and changes the numbers to make them easier to work with. Ask:

- ***What is Our Friend doing? Why does his method work?*** ("Unpack" each of Our Friend's solutions one at a time, taking care that all students understand before moving on. This looks like a lot of work, but, because the numbers are easy to work with, it is quicker than working out the solutions using traditional approaches, especially after a little practice.)

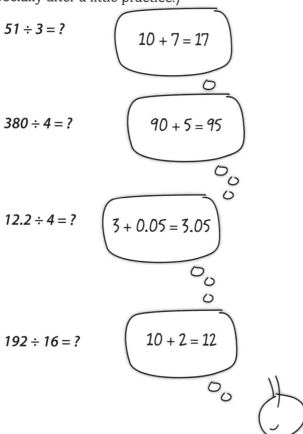

$51 \div 3 = ?$

$10 + 7 = 17$

$380 \div 4 = ?$

$90 + 5 = 95$

$12.2 \div 4 = ?$

$3 + 0.05 = 3.05$

$192 \div 16 = ?$

$10 + 2 = 12$

Our Friend is making use of the distributive property. Whether or not students know the term for that property yet, they can still understand and use it. Here's how it works.

When the problem is $51 \div 3$, Our Friend thinks that 51 is the same as $30 + 21$. Our Friend also knows that if you divide both of those numbers by 3, you'll get $10 + 7$ or 17. Draw a number bond to show this relationship to students:

$$51 \div 3 = ?$$
$$(30 \div 3) + (21 \div 3) = ?$$
$$10 \quad + \quad 7 \quad = 17$$

Using the same approach, $380 \div 4$ becomes $(360 + 20) \div 4 = 90 + 5$ or 95.

$12.2 \div 4$ is a bit trickier. Our Friend thought of this problem as $(12 + 0.20) \div 4$ because he knows 0.2 is the same as 0.20. That turns the problem into:
$(12 \div 4) + (0.20 \div 4) = ?$
$3 + 0.05 = 3.05$

For $192 \div 16$, Our Friend made the problem easier this way:
$(160 + 32) \div 16 = ?$
$(160 \div 16) + (32 \div 16) = ?$
$10 + 2 = 12$

Invite a student to draw the number bond that demonstrates how Our Friend's approach works, based on the earlier solutions.

There are other ways to solve $192 \div 16$. Suppose someone else sees that there are 3 groups of 64 in 192, and 16×4 is 64. So when they look at the problem they think $(64 + 64 + 64) \div 16$. Would this person still get the right answer? Yes! They are using a different way of looking at the problem, but they get to the same place. This is great. Be sure to always ask students to share all the different ways they solve a problem. All students benefit from seeing the variety of approaches.

Guided Conversation *continued*

If your students have worked with percents, show them this next problem. If not, you may wish to skip it. Tell students that Our Friend Yuki is at a restaurant with his friends. The bill for their food is $86. He wants to leave a 15% tip. Ask:

- *Can you see how Our Friend figured out the tip?*

$8.60 + $4.30 = $12.90
That's my tip! About $13.

- *Why is this easier than calculating 15%?*
- *Would it have made sense for Our Friend to figure 15% by taking 12% of the bill and adding to that 3% of the bill? Explain why or why not.*

Let's see if we can stretch your students' thinking a bit more. Give them the following problems—without Our Friend's hints yet—and allow a chunk of quiet time for them to work on them. Encourage students to think about ways to make these problems quicker and easier to solve.

$$99 + 99 = ?$$

$$99 + 99 + 99 + 99 + 99 = ?$$

Invite students to share their ideas about how to make these problems easier and to explain why they think their ideas work. Share Our Friend's approach. Ask students to explain why that approach works and why Our Friend has to subtract 2 at the end of the first problem.

After students have drawn their conclusions about how these "99" problems were solved, ask:

- *What is the least number of 99s you can add together so there is a 1 in the ones place of the sum?*

Behind the Math

Our Friend took 10% of the bill ($8.60) and then took half of that amount or 5% ($4.30) and added them together. It's easier to do than 15% because 10 is an easy number to work with; finding half of something is also easy.

Our Friend can get the right answer this way, but 12% and 3% aren't as easy to work with as 10% and 5%, so it makes much more sense to work with 10% and 5%.

$200 - 2 = 198$ $500 - 5 = 495$

Our Friend is making the problem easier by changing 99 + 99 to 100 + 100. In this problem, he can't just randomly add numbers without changing the result, so he subtracts 2 at the end.

The least number of 99s to get a 1 in the ones place is 9. The sum of nine 99s is equivalent to 900 − 9, which is the same as 899 − 8 = 881. (Notice this uses subtraction compensation, which was used earlier for solving 800 − 8.)

Guided Conversation *continued*

Tell students that Our Friend has another one for them, along with a hint. Ask:

- *Why do you think Our Friend is saying to make 10s? How does that help?*

    $$1 + 2 + 3 + 4 + 5 + 6 + 7 + 8 + 9 = ?$$

As always, give students lots of time to think about this. If some students still can't figure out what Our Friend is doing, let him show them the work.

Tell students that Our Friend can do the following problem in just seconds. Ask:

- *How does Our Friend solve this problem so quickly?*

    $$1 + 2 + 3 + 4 \dots 96 + 97 + 98 + 99 = ?$$

Behind the Math

Our Friend is saying to look for pairs of numbers that equal 10. It might be helpful to show these pairs by drawing arcs connecting the pairs above the problem.

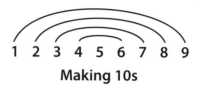

Making 10s

There are 9 numbers, so there can be 4 pairs with one number left over. If the number of digits in the problem is odd, then Our Friend knows he needs to add the number in the middle (the one without a match that makes 10) to the product of the number of pairs times 10.

Suppose someone solving this problem said they got $(4 \times 11) + 1$. Does this approach also work? Sure. They just made 4 pairs whose sum was 11, instead of 4 pairs whose sum was 10. This time the number that wasn't paired with another number was 1, so 1 had to be added to the product.

Our Friend knows that there are 99 numbers, so there will be half that many pairs of numbers that equal 100. Dividing 99 by 2 gives Our Friend 49 with 1 left over. Our Friend multiplies 49 (the number of pairs) by 100 (the number that each pair makes) to get 4900. But what about that 1 left over? In this problem, the 1 stands for 50 because there is no number to pair with 50 to make 100. So 50 must be added to the product of 49 and 100.

$$99 \div 2 = 49 \text{ pairs R 1}$$
$$49 \times 100 = 4900$$
$$\text{unpaired number is } 50$$
$$4900 + 50 = 4950$$

Activities 9-16

Visualization

Visualization is being able to "see" in the mind's eye what words and numbers are saying.

SECTION 2

Visualization

Visualization is fundamental to learning in general and to math in particular. The ability to visualize, to imagine what something looks like or what it means, is a key component of intellectual competence. It is one of the most important abilities students can develop. The student with strong visualization skills can:

- Comprehend visual images, including both abstract diagrams and realistic illustrations.

- Turn visual images in the mind, to see them from different perspectives and in different ways.

- Generate visual images while reading text.

Visualization is being able to "see" what words and numbers are saying. In other words, it's the ability to go from text to visual interpretation of the text. It's our mind doing things our eyes and hands can't do.

Why Does Visualization Matter?

Our friends Sam and Reena are in math class together. Their teacher holds up 12 candy bars and asks them to picture how many each child will get if the candy bars are being split among 4 people. Easy. Both Sam and Reena know the answer is 3. Then the teacher removes all but 3 candy bars and asks the same question.

Sam looks lost. He's not sure if they'll each get more than 1 candy bar or less than 1. Reena looks at the 3 candy bars the teacher is holding and imagines each of the 4 children getting $\frac{1}{4}$ of each of the 3 bars. She raises her hand and says, "Each will get $\frac{3}{4}$ of a candy bar."

Next the teacher says, "Imagine you are in a line of people buying movie tickets. There are 4 people in front of you and 6 people behind you. How many people are in line?" Reena pictures the situation in her mind and answers, "11." Sam just sees the numbers 4 and 6, adds them, and says, "10."

There are times when manipulatives are not available, and students need to be able to see problems in their mind. Reena can do this. She has strong visualization skills. Sam is not yet strong at math and doesn't "see" the problems the way Reena does. Regular practice with manipulatives will help students like Sam to understand the meaning behind the math. With practice, students can visualize their way to solving problems quickly and correctly, even when they don't have access to manipulatives.

ACTIVITY **9** Fractions with Pattern Blocks

Why Do This Activity?

Students get hands-on experience that helps them visualize the meaning of fractions. Using pattern blocks, students discover that a whole unit can be shown in different ways by combining different fractional parts. Equally important, students see that $\frac{1}{2}$ of one unit does not equal $\frac{1}{2}$ of another unit if the units are not of equal size to begin with. Frequent practice with manipulatives helps students build their visualization skills, but the long-term goal is for students to leave manipulatives behind and be able to visualize the answers in their minds.

Prior Knowledge: basic geometric shapes and fraction basics

Academic Vocabulary: hexagon, trapezoid, rhombus, triangle, area, perimeter, equivalent fractions, equal fractions

Rules of the Road

- Pattern blocks are called by their standard colors in this activity. If you make pattern block pieces from the copymaster on page 169, then you need to either color each shape or avoid calling shapes by their colors during the discussion.

- Standard colors for pattern block shapes are yellow hexagons, red trapezoids, blue rhombuses, and green triangles.

- In a pattern block set, two triangles are the size of one rhombus. One triangle and one rhombus together are the size of one trapezoid. Two trapezoids are the size of a hexagon.

Time: 15 minutes for Level 1; up to 20 minutes each for Levels 2 & 3

Materials & Preparation:

- Pattern blocks (or use copymaster on page 169); each student needs 3 hexagons, 6 trapezoids, 9 rhombuses, and 8 triangles. Store the sets in plastic bags for quick distribution.

- Plain paper

- Pencils

- Document camera (optional)

- Introduce Our Friend Yuki (YOU-key) to your students if they did not meet him in Activity 8.

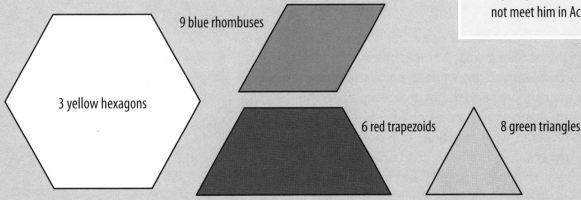

9 blue rhombuses

3 yellow hexagons

6 red trapezoids

8 green triangles

Guided Conversation

Hand out pattern blocks to each student in the quantities listed under Materials & Preparation. Give students a few minutes to explore the pattern blocks. Once they have made their own discoveries, they will be ready to follow your instructions.

Tell students to take one of each different pattern block shape. Ask:

- ***Can you place the pattern blocks in order from smallest to largest?*** (You may need to point out that the shapes should be in "reading" order, from left to right.)

- ***Do you have the same arrangement as your neighbor? If you don't, talk it through together.*** (For this problem, there is only one correct solution.)

- ***Tell your neighbor the names of the first two shapes in the row. Ask your neighbor the names of the last two shapes.*** (Help students with the names of unfamiliar shapes.)

Ask students to place a yellow hexagon on a piece of plain paper and trace around its edge. Tell them that this space is called "1 whole" or "1 unit." Ask:

- ***Can you use your other pattern blocks to fill the whole hexagon space with 2 identical pieces?***

- ***What pieces did you use to fill the whole hexagon?***

- ***Can you fill a whole hexagon space with 3 identical pieces?***

- ***Can you fill the hexagon with 4, 5, or 6 identical pieces?***

Note that it is extremely important that students hear you consistently asking or telling what 1 whole unit stands for, in whatever problem you are working on. A fraction describes how many equal parts there are in relation to the whole; it does not have any value outside of this relationship. Always think about what the whole unit is—whether it's a hexagon, trapezoid, or rhombus, as in this problem, or whether it's a pizza, an apple, or the whole planet Earth in other problems.

Behind the Math

Smallest to largest shapes:

If students need help, show them how to lay one shape over another to compare sizes.

You can fill the hexagon with these shapes:

2 red trapezoids   3 blue rhombuses   6 green rectangles

You can't fill the hexagon with 4 or 5 identical pieces.

Guided Conversation *continued*

Once students know how many of each shape make up one whole hexagon, guide them to relate the shapes to the fraction that each shape represents. Ask:

- *If it takes 2 red trapezoids to fill the hexagon, then what part of the hexagon does each trapezoid stand for?*

Write the fraction $\frac{1}{2}$ where all students can see it. Point to the 1 in the fraction and explain that each trapezoid is 1 part out of 2 equal parts (point to the 2 in the fraction) that make up the hexagon. Ask:

- *How many halves make 1 whole?*

Write the statement $\frac{1}{2} + \frac{1}{2} = \frac{2}{2}$ as you say "1 half and 1 half is the same as 2 halves." Ask students if these 2 halves completely cover the whole hexagon. If they do, then that means that 2 halves (or $\frac{2}{2}$) must equal 1.

Follow this same procedure of writing out and saying the fraction statements while asking students about the next two shapes.

- *How many blue rhombuses are needed to cover the hexagon?*
- *What part of the hexagon is each rhombus?*
- *How many thirds make 1 whole?*

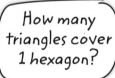

How many rhombuses cover 1 hexagon?

How many triangles cover 1 hexagon?

- *How many green triangles are needed to cover the hexagon?*
- *What part of the hexagon does each triangle show?*
- *How many sixths make 1 whole?*

Behind the Math

Two red trapezoids fill the whole hexagon, so each trapezoid shows $\frac{1}{2}$ of the whole.

Two halves make 1 whole, or $\frac{1}{2} + \frac{1}{2} = 1$ (or $\frac{2}{2}$).

Three rhombuses cover the whole hexagon. Each rhombus shows $\frac{1}{3}$ of the whole, so 3 thirds make 1 whole, or $\frac{1}{3} + \frac{1}{3} + \frac{1}{3} = 1$ (or $\frac{3}{3}$).

Six triangles cover the whole hexagon. Each triangle shows $\frac{1}{6}$ of the whole, so 6 sixths make 1 whole, or $\frac{1}{6} + \frac{1}{6} + \frac{1}{6} + \frac{1}{6} + \frac{1}{6} + \frac{1}{6} = 1$ (or $\frac{6}{6}$).

Guided Conversation

Use pattern blocks to model this problem for the class. Place 1 hexagon on the table. Completely cover it with green triangles.

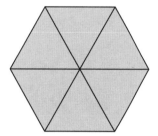

Ask:

- *What fractions are these pattern blocks illustrating?*

- *How can you write a number sentence using these fractions?* (Write all answers where everyone can see them. Keep asking until the class has given you several different ways to write the same number sentence.)

Now remove 1 triangle from the hexagon. Ask:

- *What part of the hexagon is still covered with triangles?*

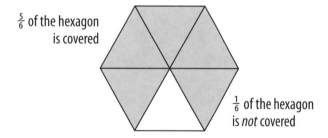

$\frac{5}{6}$ of the hexagon is covered

$\frac{1}{6}$ of the hexagon is *not* covered

Tell students you're going to show them another figure. Cover the hexagon using a green triangle, a blue rhombus, and a red trapezoid. Students may want to make this same model using their own pattern blocks. Ask:

- *Is the whole hexagon covered?*

- *What part of the hexagon is covered?*

- *Is any part of the hexagon not covered?*

Now cover the hexagon with 2 blue rhombuses, and have students do the same. Ask:

Behind the Math

The whole hexagon is covered by 6 triangles. There are several ways that students can express this mathematically:

$$\frac{1}{6} + \frac{1}{6} + \frac{1}{6} + \frac{1}{6} + \frac{1}{6} + \frac{1}{6} = \frac{6}{6}$$
$$\frac{1}{6} + \frac{1}{6} + \frac{1}{6} + \frac{1}{6} + \frac{1}{6} + \frac{1}{6} = 1$$

Someone may also answer: $6 \times \frac{1}{6} = 1$

Or, because this is 1 whole unit, students may use any other fraction in which the numerator and denominator are the same number, such as $\frac{2}{2}$, $\frac{3}{3}$, or even $\frac{12}{12}$.

$\frac{5}{6}$ of the hexagon is covered with triangles.

Similarly, you could say $\frac{0}{6}$ of the hexagon is *not* covered.

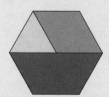

Yes, the whole hexagon is covered. That can be expressed as $\frac{2}{2}$, $\frac{3}{3}$, $\frac{6}{6}$, or any other fraction that means 1. No part of the hexagon is not covered.

Guided Conversation *continued*

- *What part of the hexagon is covered?*
- *What part of the hexagon is not covered?*
- *Can you finish covering the hexagon using triangles? How many triangles does it take?*
- *What fraction of the hexagon do those triangles make?*
- *Can you write a number sentence that describes how the two triangle fractions equal the rhombus fraction?*

If they need help for the last two questions, show students what Our Friend is thinking.

Will $\frac{1}{6}$ be in the number sentence?

Behind the Math

Two-thirds ($\frac{2}{3}$) of the hexagon is covered.
One-third ($\frac{1}{3}$) is not covered.

Adding 2 green triangles completely covers the hexagon.

The last 2 triangles make up $\frac{2}{6}$ or $\frac{1}{3}$ of the hexagon.

Walk students through this as needed. We know that the empty space was $\frac{1}{3}$ of the hexagon. We filled it with 2 triangles. Each triangle shows $\frac{1}{6}$ of the hexagon, so now we know that $\frac{1}{6} + \frac{1}{6} = \frac{1}{3}$.

ACTIVITY ⑨ Fractions with Pattern Blocks: LEVEL 3

Guided Conversation

Now it's time to see if your students are really paying attention to the all-important question, "What whole unit is this fraction part of?"

Place 2 blue rhombuses on a hexagon so their sides are touching, as you did for the $\frac{2}{3}$ demonstration in Level 2. Now, place a red trapezoid on top of the rhombuses to make the figure shown at right. Ask students to build the same model at their desks.

Tell students to listen carefully as you ask the following questions:

- *What part of the yellow hexagon is covered by the red trapezoid?*
- *What part of the yellow hexagon is not covered by any shape?*

Be prepared for plenty of wait time as you move into the trickier questions. Ask:

Behind the Math

Half ($\frac{1}{2}$) of the hexagon is covered by the red trapezoid.

One-third ($\frac{1}{3}$) of the hexagon is not covered by any shape.

Guided Conversation *continued*

- *What part of the 2 blue rhombuses is not covered by the red trapezoid?* (Don't acknowledge right away if you hear the correct answer of $\frac{1}{4}$. Keep asking until you are sure students have said all of the answers that they feel are correct. Encourage students to discuss these questions with each other as a class.)

Before you confirm the right answer, repeat the question and have Our Friend give a hint.

> What's the whole unit?

When all students understand that the 2 rhombuses equal 1 whole unit, ask:

- *What shape do you need to add to hide the rest of the 2-rhombus unit?*
- *What fraction of the 2-rhombus unit is covered when you add that triangle?*
- *What fraction of the 2-rhombus unit is the triangle?*

Now cover the hexagon with a trapezoid, a rhombus, and a triangle, and have students do the same. Then ask:

- *What fraction of the hexagon does each shape show?*

Next, ask students to write an addition number sentence that describes the model they just built. The sum of the numbers in the sentence should be 1. When students have had a chance to do this, ask:

- *Does everyone have the same answer?* (There may be variations in order of addends, but there is only one correct answer.)

Invite students to fill in the hexagon using other shape combinations. For each combination, ask students to write the fraction of the hexagon that each shape represents. Then have them write number sentences that represent that combination of shapes. Give them time to figure out a few different combinations.

Behind the Math

This is where students really need to pay attention to what is being asked. Two rhombuses together represent 1 whole unit. The question is asking what part of the *2 rhombuses* is not covered (not the hexagon). The answer is one-fourth ($\frac{1}{4}$). Help students to see this by counting up the number of triangles (4) that would cover 2 rhombuses. Three triangles cover 1 red trapezoid, so the trapezoid covers $\frac{3}{4}$ of the 2 rhombuses.

Adding a triangle hides both rhombuses completely and makes the fraction $\frac{4}{4}$, or 1. The triangle is $\frac{1}{4}$ of the 2-rhombus unit.

From above, this pattern block model will look the same as in the previous problem, but the stack will be shorter and the colors will be a little different. Answers:
trapezoid $= \frac{1}{2}$ of the hexagon
rhombus $= \frac{1}{3}$ of the hexagon
triangle $= \frac{1}{6}$ of the hexagon

Students just wrote the fraction of the hexagon that each shape represents, and they know that these three shapes add up to 1 whole hexagon. It's a small step from there to recognize this number sentence:
$\frac{1}{2} + \frac{1}{3} + \frac{1}{6} = 1$

Some example answers:

3 rhombuses: $\frac{1}{3} + \frac{1}{3} + \frac{1}{3} = 1$

2 rhombuses + 2 triangles: $\frac{1}{3} + \frac{1}{3} + \frac{1}{6} + \frac{1}{6} = 1$

1 trapezoid + 3 triangles: $\frac{1}{2} + \frac{1}{6} + \frac{1}{6} + \frac{1}{6} = 1$

Guided Conversation *continued*

Tell students it's time to change the unit measure. (It may help to suggest that this is a game where the rules keep changing, so they need to listen well.) Ask:

- *If the rhombus is 1 whole unit, then what part of the rhombus is the triangle?* (Encourage students to use their pattern block shapes to figure this out. As needed, guide students to recognize that the rhombus now represents 1, the way that the hexagon did earlier.)

- *If the trapezoid is 1 whole unit, then what part of the trapezoid is the triangle?*

Repeat the answers: The triangle is $\frac{1}{2}$ of the rhombus. But that same triangle is $\frac{1}{3}$ of the trapezoid. Ask:

- *How can the same shape be two different fractions?*

(Give students time to think before helping the class come up with the explanation.)

Ask students if these two statements are true:

- *The triangle is $\frac{1}{2}$ of the rhombus.*
- *The trapezoid is $\frac{1}{2}$ of the hexagon.*

Give students time to think, to work with their pattern blocks, and to talk to each other. Don't give the right answer yet. When most students seem convinced that both statements are true, say:

- *I'm confused. How can the triangle and the trapezoid both equal $\frac{1}{2}$?*

- *If both shapes are $\frac{1}{2}$, does that mean they are equal to each other?*

Make students convince you that a triangle does not equal a trapezoid, even though both can equal $\frac{1}{2}$. Keep pointing at Our Friend's hint, "What's the whole unit?" Guide them to realize that you have to know the answer to "one-half of what?" for $\frac{1}{2}$ to have any value at all.

Behind the Math

The triangle is $\frac{1}{2}$ of the rhombus.

The triangle is $\frac{1}{3}$ of the trapezoid.

It depends which whole shape you're comparing the triangle to. The triangle is $\frac{1}{2}$ of the rhombus, $\frac{1}{3}$ of the trapezoid, and $\frac{1}{6}$ of the hexagon! It could even be another fraction of a different whole, couldn't it?

Both statements are true.

The triangle is $\frac{1}{2}$ of a different shape than the rhombus is. The two shapes are not equal. Halves are only equal if they are $\frac{1}{2}$ of the same whole unit.

Guided Conversation *continued*

Say that it's time to change the units again. The following questions deal with whole units that are not equal to 1 hexagon. Remind students to use their pattern blocks to help find answers.

- *Which pattern block shows $\frac{1}{6}$ when you use 2 hexagons put together as 1 whole unit? How do you know?*

- *If 3 red trapezoids show $\frac{1}{2}$ of some unknown shape, then what number of trapezoids would show 1 whole unit?*

- *For this same unknown shape, what is the fewest number of pieces that would show 1 whole unit? What pieces are they?*

Now try some problems that will help students visualize division. You don't need to point out that these are division problems. Phrase the questions in terms of how many parts make up the number. Start out by asking:

- *How many halves are in $2\frac{1}{2}$?* (Have students use the pattern block pieces to find the answer. Remind them to use 1 yellow hexagon as 1 whole unit.)

Try some more. Tell students to answer these problems after they use the pattern blocks to illustrate the value they are being asked to find. Ask:

- *How many thirds are in $2\frac{1}{2}$?* (Remind students to first think about how many $\frac{1}{3}$s are in 1 hexagon.)

- *Does $2\frac{1}{2}$ divide into thirds evenly?*

Behind the Math

If 2 hexagons show 1 whole, then a rhombus shows $\frac{1}{6}$ of this whole because it takes 6 rhombuses to cover the 2 hexagons.

If 3 trapezoids show $\frac{1}{2}$ of the unknown whole shape, then 6 trapezoids show the whole shape.

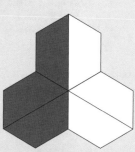

The fewest number of pieces you could use to show this shape would be 3 yellow hexagons. They may be arranged as a "snowflake" as shown above, or in a line (the problem doesn't specify).

Two hexagons plus 1 trapezoid (which represents $2\frac{1}{2}$) would contain 5 trapezoids, so there are five $\frac{1}{2}$s in $2\frac{1}{2}$ or $2\frac{1}{2} \div \frac{1}{2} = 5$. (It's okay if students do not initially make the connection that they are solving a division problem.)

A blue rhombus stands for $\frac{1}{3}$ of a hexagon. It takes 7 rhombuses to cover the shape that shows $2\frac{1}{2}$, but there is still a portion left uncovered. So $2\frac{1}{2}$ can't be divided evenly into thirds.

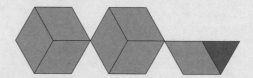

Guided Conversation *continued*

Ask students:

- *Can you write a number sentence for $2\frac{1}{2}$ divided into thirds?*

- *How do you write the leftover part?*

Students (and many adults) may be confused by the fact that you can end up with $\frac{1}{2}$ in your answer when you divided by 3. Ask:

- *Why isn't the answer for the leftover shape $\frac{1}{3}$?*

Behind the Math

The number sentence includes a fraction, $\frac{1}{2}$, to show the leftover part:

$$2\frac{1}{2} \div \frac{1}{3} = 7\frac{1}{2}$$

The triangle shape is $\frac{1}{2}$ of the shape we were dividing by. Since we were looking for how many $\frac{1}{3}$ pieces were in the whole shape, the answer is 7 shapes that stand for $\frac{1}{3}$, plus half of a shape that stands for $\frac{1}{3}$—or $7\frac{1}{2}$ shapes.

Demonstrate the answer using pattern blocks.

Here's another way to think about this: The space left over (not covered) is a triangle shape. A triangle shape is $\frac{1}{2}$ of a rhombus shape.

ACTIVITY 10 Forming Equal Parts

Why Do This Activity?

These activities improve students' conceptual understanding of fractions through the use of concrete manipulatives that help them "see" the fractions. Students start out by demonstrating to themselves that the same shape can be divided into four parts two different ways. They go on to demonstrate that different shapes can be equal fractions, as long as the fraction shapes have the same portion of the whole shape. Students discover that this is true even when the shapes are irregular.

Prior Knowledge: basic geometric shapes and fraction basics

Academic Vocabulary: equal parts of a whole, equivalent fractions, equal fractions, diagonal, area, and perimeter

Rules of the Road

- Draw lines to show how to divide each big square into equal parts. Make as many equal parts as the activity sheet tells you to make.

- Begin at the bold line on each big square.

- You can make more than one line.

Time: 10 minutes each for Levels 1 & 2; up to 20 minutes for Level 3

Materials & Preparation:

- Rulers

- Pencils

- Scissors

- Activity Sheet 10A, 1 copy for each student (page 96)

- Activity Sheet 10B, 2 copies for each student (page 97)

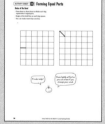

Activity Sheet **10A**

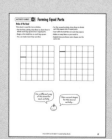

Activity Sheet **10B**

Guided Conversation

The goal in Level 1 is for students to recognize that there are at least two ways to divide the same graphic into 4 parts of equal shape and size.

Give each student a copy of Activity Sheet 10A, a pencil, ruler, and scissors. Have all students perform this activity independently. Ask them to place their pencils on the bold line already in each drawing. Then, have them use this bold line as part of one line and ask them to draw two lines that divide the large square into 4 equal parts. Have students check with their neighbors to see if they drew the same lines. Ask:

- *Can you have different drawings and both be right?*

Ask students to take a pair of scissors and cut along the lines that they have drawn in each square. Ask:

- *What fraction of the whole square is each small shape?*

- *When you stack the 4 pieces from one square on top of the others, are they the same size and shape?*

- *Do all the shapes from both drawings stand for the same fraction of the whole square, even if they are different shapes? How can that be?*

Behind the Math

Most students will come up with these two solutions for Activity Sheet 10A, which form 4 pieces of equal size and shape for each large square.

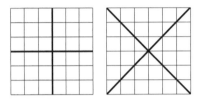

In this case, there is only one correct solution. Make sure students think about this question, however, because Levels 2 and 3 present challenges with multiple solutions.

Each small shape is $\frac{1}{4}$ of a whole square.

Pieces from the same square are the same size and shape.

Yes, all the shapes are the same fraction of the whole square. Students may not yet be able to explain this in terms of the shapes having equal areas. That's okay. The point is to get them thinking about the cut squares and the cut triangles being equivalent—one-fourth of the whole square—even though they have different shapes.

Guided Conversation

In Level 2, students again divide squares into equal parts two different ways. They then compare the number of small grid squares on each divided part to conclude that the two shapes are the same size, and, therefore, they are the same fraction of the whole.

Hand out one copy of Activity Sheet 10B to each student. Tell students to divide the two grids into 6 equal parts, using the bold line segment to start their first line. When students have finished, have them cut out the shapes they've created within each large square. Ask:

- *What fraction of the whole square is each shape you've drawn? How do you know?*

Point out that both shapes are the same fraction of the same whole. So they are equal. But they look different. Ask:

- *Can you prove that the short, wide rectangle is equal to the long, skinny rectangle?*

Behind the Math

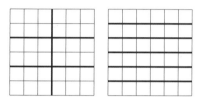

Each shape is $\frac{1}{6}$ of the whole square because there are 6 of these shapes in the whole square.

Counting the small squares in one example of each shape shows that they each have 6 small squares. This shows that they are the same size, even though they are different shapes.

Hand out another copy of Activity Sheet 10B to each student. This time, ask students to draw lines to divide the two squares into 4 equal parts (fourths), starting with the bold line on each square. Give them some time to work on this, and then ask:

- *Is it harder to make fourths with these lines than with the ones on Activity Sheet 10A? Why?*

Behind the Math

It is more difficult. Unlike the activity they completed on Activity Sheet 10A, it takes more than a couple of straight lines to divide the squares into 4 equal parts, starting with the lines indicated.

Guided Conversation *continued*

Have students compare their drawings on Activity Sheet 10B with their neighbors' work to see whether their drawings match. Ask:

- *If your drawings don't match, can they both be right?*

(Have several students explain how they would know if they drew 4 parts that are each $\frac{1}{4}$ of the original square.)

Have students cut out the parts they made for each square.

- *Are the 4 parts equal in size and shape?*
- *If the 4 parts are different shapes, are they still fourths? How can you tell?*

If your students have had basic geometry, continue with the next questions. Ask:

- *What is the perimeter of the original square?*
- *You divided the original square into 4 parts. Is the perimeter of each of those 4 parts $\frac{1}{4}$ of the original perimeter?*
- *Are the perimeters of the 4 parts equal to each other?*
- *What is the area of the original square, in square units?*
- *Are the areas of each of the 4 parts you formed equal?*
- *Is the area of each fourth that you formed $\frac{1}{4}$ of the original area?*

Behind the Math

The example below shows one of many possible correct answers for the two squares. Students are correct as long as each of the parts they draw has 9 small square units, based on the 36 units in the whole square.

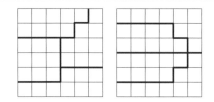

The 4 shapes from 1 square may not be the same. The shapes are equal in size if they have the same number of small units. You may need to point out that a diagonal drawn in any unit divides that individual unit into 2 equal parts, each $\frac{1}{2}$ of a unit. Two of these $\frac{1}{2}$ units together are equal to 1 unit.

The perimeter of the original square is 24 units. The perimeter of any piece that makes up $\frac{1}{4}$ of the original will always be equal to more than $\frac{1}{4}$ of the perimeter (more than 6 units). The perimeters of each piece are not necessarily equal to each other.

The area of the original square is 36 square units. The area of each of the 4 parts is exactly 9 square units. This demonstrates that 9 is $\frac{1}{4}$ of 36.

Forming Equal Parts

Rules of the Road

- Draw lines to show how to divide each big square into 4 equal parts.
- Begin at the bold line on each big square.
- You can make more than one line.

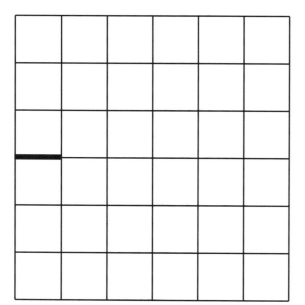

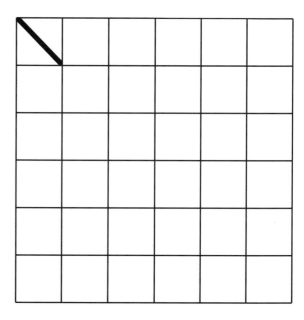

A ruler helps!

Draw lightly at first so you can erase if you change your mind.

Every Child Can Do Math © Crystal Springs Books

Forming Equal Parts

Rules of the Road

This sheet is used for two activities.

- For the first activity, draw lines to show how to divide each big square into 6 equal parts.
- Begin at the bold line on each big square.
- You can make more than one line.

- For the second activity, draw lines to divide each big square into 4 equal parts.
- Start with the bold line on each big square.
- Make as many lines as you need to.
- Explain how you know your shapes are the same size.

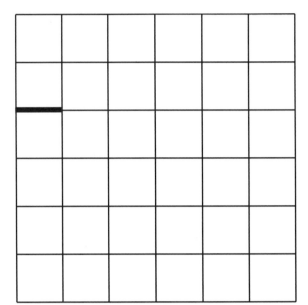

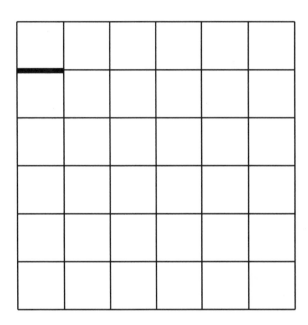

Use a different copy of this sheet for each activity.

I like unusual shapes for the second activity...

ACTIVITY ⑪ Parts of a Whole

Why Do This Activity?

Students use materials to imagine fractional parts based on a whole. Then they approach fractions from the other direction by imagining the whole based on a fractional part. By exploring fractions of different-sized wholes, students realize that the same pattern block piece can stand for different fractions, and that different pieces can stand for the same fraction—it all depends on the size of the whole! Later, when students work with fraction number sentences, they can rely on the understanding gained from working with these manipulatives.

Prior Knowledge: basic geometric shapes, part-whole relationship, and fraction basics

Academic Vocabulary: rhombus, triangle, equivalent fractions, equal fractions

Time: 10 minutes for Level 1; up to 20 minutes for Level 2

Materials & Preparation:

- 1 tangram set for each student, plus an extra set for demonstration. Or copy the Tangram Set (page 170) on cardstock for each student.

- 1 set of pattern blocks or pattern block pieces (page 169) for each student (6 green triangles, 4 blue rhombuses, 2 red trapezoids, 1 yellow hexagon), or containers of pattern blocks for groups of students to share

- Activity Sheets 11A and 11B, 1 copy of each for each student (pages 102–103)

- Document camera or other method of displaying activity sheets and materials during discussion

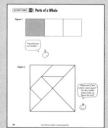

Activity Sheet **11A**

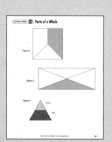

Activity Sheet **11B**

Guided Conversation

Give each student a tangram set and a copy of Activity Sheet 11A. Set up your copy of Activity Sheet 11A where students can follow along, and have a tangram set nearby for demonstrations.

Point out that, in the first diagram on Activity Sheet 11A, a large rectangle is divided into 3 equal parts. Ask:

- *What part of the whole rectangle is shaded?*
- *What part of the whole rectangle is not shaded?*

Next, point out the drawing that shows the outline of the tangram pieces. Read Our Friend Yuki's questions:

- *What part of the whole is each piece? Can the smaller shapes help me figure this out?* (Tell students that it may help to use their tangram puzzle pieces to figure this out.)

Give students lots of time to work on this problem. Then invite students to give answers and to explain how they came up with their answers. Take time with the answers, and encourage more than one student to answer fully, even if an answer is the same as one that was already given.

If students seem to be struggling, suggest they join with a few classmates so they have more tangram pieces to work with. Then ask:

- *How many pieces the size of one small triangle would you need to cover the whole big square?*

Behind the Math

$\frac{1}{3}$ of the whole rectangle is shaded.

$\frac{2}{3}$ of the whole rectangle is not shaded.

Each of the two small triangles is equal to $\frac{1}{16}$ of the whole square.

The medium triangle, square, and rhombus are each equal to $\frac{2}{16}$ or $\frac{1}{8}$ of the whole square.

Each of the two large triangles is equal to $\frac{1}{4}$ of the whole square.

It takes 16 of the small tangram triangles to completely cover the whole large square. Once students have figured this out, have them count the number of small triangles that make up each larger shape, to answer the original question.

Guided Conversation continued

Once everyone is comfortable with the solution to Our Friend's question, ask:

- *Do any pieces represent the same fraction of the whole square? If so, which ones?* (Remember to name the "whole" whenever you are working with fractions. It is important for students to understand that you must know what the whole is in order to know what the fraction means.)

- *Can different shapes represent the same fraction of the whole square? How can this be?* (Allow lots of time for students to figure out how to explain this. Suggest they use tangram pieces to show how three different shapes show the same fraction of the same whole.)

- *What 2 tangram pieces equal $\frac{3}{16}$ of the whole square when they are added together?* (Try to get students to come up with all the possible options. Have them use their tangram pieces to show how they came up with each answer.)

- *Can you write your solution as a number sentence?*

Behind the Math

Yes; see the list on page 99 for pieces that represent the same fraction of the whole square.

Behind the Math

Yes, different shapes can show the same fraction. Students can use the 2 small triangles to show that the medium triangle, the square, and the rhombus each equal 2 small triangles, which is $\frac{2}{16}$ (or $\frac{1}{8}$) of the whole tangram square.

If either of the small triangles ($\frac{1}{16}$) is added to the medium triangle, square, or rhombus ($\frac{2}{16}$ or $\frac{1}{8}$), then the resulting shape equals $\frac{3}{16}$ of the whole square. The number sentence can be written two ways:

$$\frac{1}{16} + \frac{2}{16} = \frac{3}{16}$$
$$\frac{1}{16} + \frac{1}{8} = \frac{3}{16}$$

ACTIVITY ⑪ Parts of a Whole: LEVEL 2

Guided Conversation

Give each student a copy of Activity Sheet 11B. Have pattern blocks (or pattern block pieces) available to hand out a little later on. You may want to assemble sets as listed in Materials & Preparation on page 98, or place containers of pattern blocks where groups of students can easily share them.

To start, you'll be discussing Figures 3 and 4 on the activity sheet. Ask:

- *What if someone says that the shaded part of the square in Figure 3 is $\frac{1}{3}$ of the square. Is she right? Explain.* (Call on at least three people to explain their thinking. If anyone says his answer is the same as one already given, say, "That's okay; I'd still like to hear you explain it.")

Behind the Math

No, she's not. The shaded area can't be $\frac{1}{3}$ of the whole square because the 3 parts are not equal.

Guided Conversation *continued*

- *Can you figure out what part of the square the shaded part really is?* (If students need a hint, suggest that they draw in more lines to form 8 equal triangles.)

- *What if someone says that the shaded part of the rectangle in Figure 4 is $\frac{1}{4}$ of the rectangle? Is he right? Explain.* (If students are not able to explain their reasoning, suggest they draw two more lines, one vertical and one horizontal, through the point where the diagonals cross, to form 8 equal triangles. If students are still not convinced, then they can cut out the triangles to see they are the same.)

Distribute pattern blocks to students.

Tell students that the large triangle in Figure 5 was drawn by tracing a green triangle above a red trapezoid using pattern block pieces. Ask:

- *If your neighbor says the green triangle is $\frac{1}{4}$ of the whole large triangle, is she correct? Explain.* (Encourage students to use pattern blocks to make the figure and to solve the problem. Ask students to demonstrate how they know their answer is correct.)

- *Can you make a triangle that is exactly $\frac{1}{9}$ green? Trace around the shapes to show your answer.* (Tell students they may use any of their pattern blocks. Make sure all students have a chance to figure this out on their own.)

- *Now can you do the same thing to make a triangle that is $\frac{1}{2}$ green?* (Give students lots of time. If they get stuck, point out that this triangle does not have to be the same size as the last one.)

- *Can you make a triangle that is $\frac{1}{3}$ green? Can you write a number sentence for this triangle?*

Behind the Math

The shaded part is $\frac{3}{8}$ of the whole square.

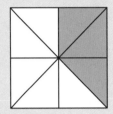

The shaded part of Figure 4 is $\frac{1}{4}$ of the rectangle. The 4 parts are equal in size (area) even though they have different shapes.

Yes, the green triangle is $\frac{1}{4}$ of the whole triangle. You can tell because it takes 4 green triangles to cover the large triangle.

A triangle that is $\frac{1}{9}$ green would be made up of 1 green triangle, 2 red trapezoids, and 1 blue rhombus.

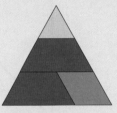

A triangle that is $\frac{1}{2}$ green could be made up of 2 green triangles and 1 blue rhombus.

A triangle that is $\frac{1}{3}$ green can be made several ways:

3 green triangles and 3 blue rhombuses
$(\frac{1}{9} + \frac{1}{9} + \frac{1}{9} + \frac{2}{9} + \frac{2}{9} + \frac{2}{9} = 1)$

3 green triangles and 2 red trapezoids
$(\frac{1}{9} + \frac{1}{9} + \frac{1}{9} + \frac{1}{3} + \frac{1}{3} = 1)$

3 green triangles and 1 yellow hexagon
$(\frac{1}{9} + \frac{1}{9} + \frac{1}{9} + \frac{2}{3} = 1)$

Parts of a Whole

Figure 1

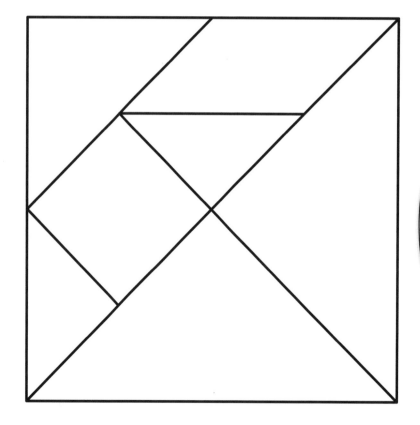

3 equal pieces, one shaded . . .

Figure 2

What part of the whole is each piece? Can the smaller shapes help me figure this out?

Every Child Can Do Math © Crystal Springs Books

Parts of a Whole

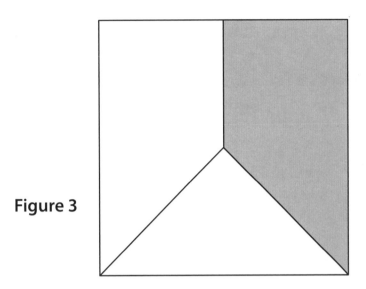

Figure 3

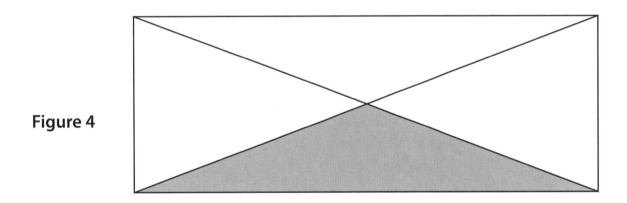

Figure 4

Figure 5

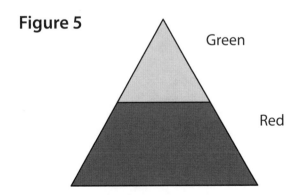

Green

Red

ACTIVITY ⑫ Tangram Shapes

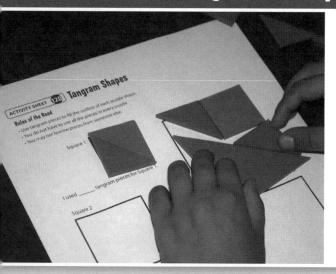

Why Do This Activity?

Solving tangram puzzles boosts students' ability to visualize pictorial solutions through the use of concrete, physical puzzle pieces. Plus, tangrams are fun! As students' skills develop, they start visualizing where each tangram piece goes, before placing it into a solution. Students may not realize that they're also exploring congruent and similar shapes. No matter what your students' entry level, you can help them develop their visualization skills by asking good questions.

Prior Knowledge: basic geometric shapes

Academic Vocabulary: tangram, square, rectangle, rhombus, parallelogram, trapezoid, quadrilateral, congruent and similar figures, attribute, area, perimeter, and ratio (Some terms are used only in Levels 2 & 3.)

Rules of the Road

- Use tangram pieces to fill the outline of each puzzle shape.

- You do not have to use all the pieces in every puzzle.

- You may not borrow pieces from someone else.

Time: 15 minutes for Level 1; up to 20 minutes each for Levels 2 & 3

Materials & Preparation:

- 1 tangram set for each student, plus one tangram set to use for demonstration; or make tangram pieces by printing the Tangram Set (page 170) on cardstock, then cutting out

- About 12 inches of lightweight string (optional)

- Activity Sheets, 1 copy each for each student, plus a set for demonstration (pages 109–113): for Level 1, 12A, 12B, and 12C; for Level 2, 12D; for Level 3, 12E

- Document camera or other method of displaying activity sheets and tangrams during discussion

Activity Sheet **12A**

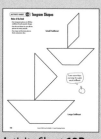

Activity Sheet **12B**

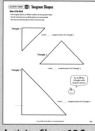

Activity Sheet **12C**

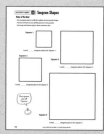

Activity Sheet **12D**

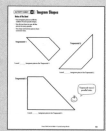

Activity Sheet **12E**

Guided Conversation

You may already have tangram sets, but if you don't, you can make laminated paper or cardstock sets using the Tangram Set copymaster (page 170). Use resealable bags or envelopes to hold each tangram set.

Give a tangram set to each student. Let them have a few minutes to explore the tangram sets before you begin the discussion. Discuss the attributes of the shapes with students.

After students have finished exploring their tangram sets, give them copies of Activity Sheets 12A and 12B. Tell them to use their tangram sets to fill in each puzzle picture on the two activity sheets. Review the Rules of the Road with your students.

After students have had ample time to work through the tree and sailboat puzzle pictures, ask the following questions:

- *Which of the three puzzle pictures was the easiest to make? Which was hardest? What makes them easy or hard?* (Encourage students to use tangram pieces to demonstrate their answers, if that's helpful.)

- *How many solutions did you find for the tree?*

- *Was it possible to make the tree trunk more than one way? Why or why not?*

- *Is there more than one way to make each sailboat?* (In mathematics, there is a difference between finding *a* solution and *the* solution. Tell students it's best to include *all* solutions they can find, when they're asked to find *the* solution.)

Behind the Math

When you are working with students to develop their visualization skills it helps to:

- Use concrete materials, like the tangram sets.

- Use diagrams and drawings, as on the activity sheets.

- Use good coaching questions, as suggested in Guided Conversation.

- Give them lots of time to figure out things on their own.

- Tell them when you see them doing something that models good visual thinking.

- Provide help for struggling students and challenge advanced students, so no one stays frustrated or bored for long.

Students probably found the tree to be the easiest and the large sailboat to be the hardest puzzle to solve. Solving the puzzles requires imagining "invisible lines" between tangram shapes in each puzzle picture. The tree has only one invisible line; the sailboats have several.

The tree has one solution. You can't make the tree trunk more than one way; although two small triangles can make the tree trunk, you need one of those triangles to make the top of the tree.

Solution for Activity Sheet 12A: Tree

Each sailboat has more than one solution. Here are two examples for each.

Solutions for Activity Sheet 12B; other solutions are possible.

Small sailboat

Small sailboat

Large sailboats

Guided Conversation *continued*

Hand out Activity Sheet 12C. Have students use their tangram sets to make each triangle on the sheet. Tell them to write down how many tangram pieces they used for each triangle. After students have had plenty of time to solve the triangle puzzles, ask:

- *How many tangram pieces did you use to make each triangle?*

- *Can you find more than one solution for each triangle? How do you know that they are all solutions?*
(You may want to introduce or review the term *congruent* in this context. Solutions for the same triangle are congruent—that is, they are the same shape and size. When you place one solution on the other, they overlap exactly.)

Behind the Math

Solutions for Activity Sheet 12C; other solutions are possible.

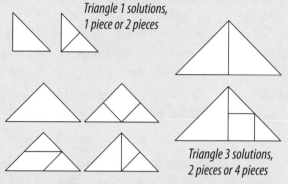

Triangle 1 solutions,
1 piece or 2 pieces

Triangle 3 solutions,
2 pieces or 4 pieces

Triangle 2 solutions,
1 piece or 3 pieces

Each of the triangles can be made using different pieces, so each one has more than one solution. You know they are all solutions for the same triangle because they all have the same shape and size (they are congruent).

ACTIVITY 12 Tangram Shapes: LEVEL 2

Guided Conversation

Hand out Activity Sheet 12D. Have students use their tangram sets to make each square on the sheet, and ask them to write down how many tangram pieces they used to make each square.

After they've had plenty of time to work on solving the square puzzles, ask the following questions:

- *Can you tell me some different ways you made a figure equal in size to Square 1?*

- *If you had multiple solutions, are the solutions congruent? How do you know?* (Give students time to remember what they did with the triangles to prove congruency.)

- *Now think about when you tried to form Square 2. Were there any tangram pieces that you could set aside right away because you knew you wouldn't use them?*

Behind the Math

Square 1 has two solutions: the square piece and the two small triangles put together. Students can prove the solutions are congruent by placing them one on top of the other. The resulting squares are the same size and shape.

You can set aside the rhombus and the two large triangles because they don't fit within the outline of Square 2.

Solutions for Activity Sheet 12D; other solutions are possible for some squares.

Square 1 solutions,
1 piece or 2 pieces

Square 2 solution,
3 pieces

Guided Conversation *continued*

- *If yes, which pieces were they and how did you know?*
- *For Square 3, did anyone find a solution that uses only triangular shapes?*

The next set of questions asks students to compare Square 1 and Square 3. You'll want to choose questions that reinforce and apply geometry terms your students are already familiar with. Ask:

- *Are Square 1 and Square 3 congruent? Why do you think so?*

- *Are Square 1 and Square 3 similar? Why do you think so?* (Remind students that items are similar if they are the same shape but not the same size.)

- *How do the sides of the smaller square (Square 1) compare to the sides of the larger square (Square 3)?* (Encourage students to use their tangram pieces to find the answer.)

- *Now think about the area of these two squares. If the side of Square 3 is twice the length of the side of Square 1, does that mean its area is twice as great?* (Give everyone time to think about this question, and then suggest that they use their tangram pieces to see how many of Square 1 would fit inside Square 3.)

- *Let's think about the perimeter of these two squares. If you had a string to wrap around Square 1 and another string to go around Square 3, how would the lengths of those strings compare?* (Provide string if it's useful to students, or suggest that they use the edge of a piece of paper to measure off the perimeters.)

- *What is the ratio of the perimeter of Square 1 to the perimeter of Square 3? What is the ratio of their areas?*

Behind the Math

Square 3 solutions, 2 pieces or 4 pieces

Squares 1 and 3 are not congruent because they are different sizes.

Squares 1 and 3 are similar because they have the same shape but not the same size.

The sides of Square 1 are half the length of the sides of Square 3. Or you could say that the sides of Square 3 are twice the length of the sides of Square 1.

The area of Square 3 (the larger square) is 4 times the area of Square 1 (the smaller square), not twice. This is an opportunity for students to visualize the meaning of area being measured in "square units."

The string around Square 3 would be 2 times the length of the string around Square 1. Another way to say this is that the string around Square 1 is half the length of the string around Square 3.

The ratio of the perimeter of Square 1 to the perimeter of Square 3 is 1 : 2. The ratio of the area of Square 1 to the area of Square 3 is 1 : 4.

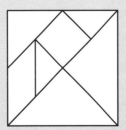

Square 4 solution, 7 pieces

Guided Conversation

Give each student a copy of Activity Sheet 12E and a set of tangram pieces. After students have spent some time on the activity sheet, ask the following questions:

- *For Trapezoid 1, which tangram pieces can you set aside right away?*

- *How do you know these pieces are not part of a solution?*

- *How many different ways can you make Trapezoid 1?*

- *Can you use different pieces to make a solution that is similar to Trapezoid 1 (same shape, different size)?* (Give students time to work on this. Ask them to repeat the definition of *similar* as it applies to shapes. If they get stuck, remind them that they may use any tangram pieces to form a solution that is similar to Trapezoid 1.)

- *Can you make Trapezoid 2 using 2 pieces? How about using 3 pieces?*

- *How many ways can you make Trapezoid 3?*

- *What attributes do all three trapezoids have in common? Make a list.*

Review with students the definition of a quadrilateral as a shape with four sides. Then ask:

- *How many different quadrilaterals can you make using all 7 tangram pieces?* (As students discover each one, ask them to name the type of quadrilateral it is, such as parallelogram, square, trapezoid, or rectangle.)

Behind the Math

You can set aside the two largest triangles because they don't fit inside the outline of Trapezoid 1.

Trapezoid 1 has two solutions. A similar trapezoid of larger size can be made by using the large triangle and medium triangle in the same layout as the secoond solution for Trapezoid 2.

Trapezoid 1 solutions, 2 pieces

Trapezoid 2 solutions, 2 pieces or 3 pieces

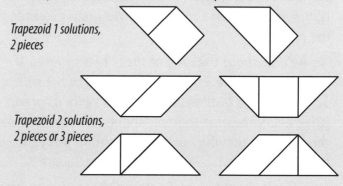

Trapezoid 3 solutions, 4 pieces

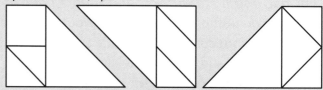

All of the trapezoids have four sides and two of those sides are parallel. Students may list other common attributes, such as all three trapezoids can be made with tangram pieces.

Six quadrilaterals that are made using all 7 tangram pieces are shown.

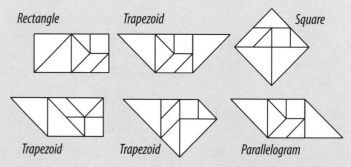

Rectangle *Trapezoid* *Square*

Trapezoid *Trapezoid* *Parallelogram*

Tangram Shapes

Rules of the Road

- Use tangram pieces to fill the outline of each puzzle shape.
- You do not have to use all the pieces in every puzzle.
- You may not borrow pieces from someone else.

I see more pieces than the outline shows.

Tree

Tangram Shapes

Rules of the Road

- Use tangram pieces to fill the outline of each puzzle shape.
- You do not have to use all the pieces in every puzzle.
- You may not borrow pieces from someone else.

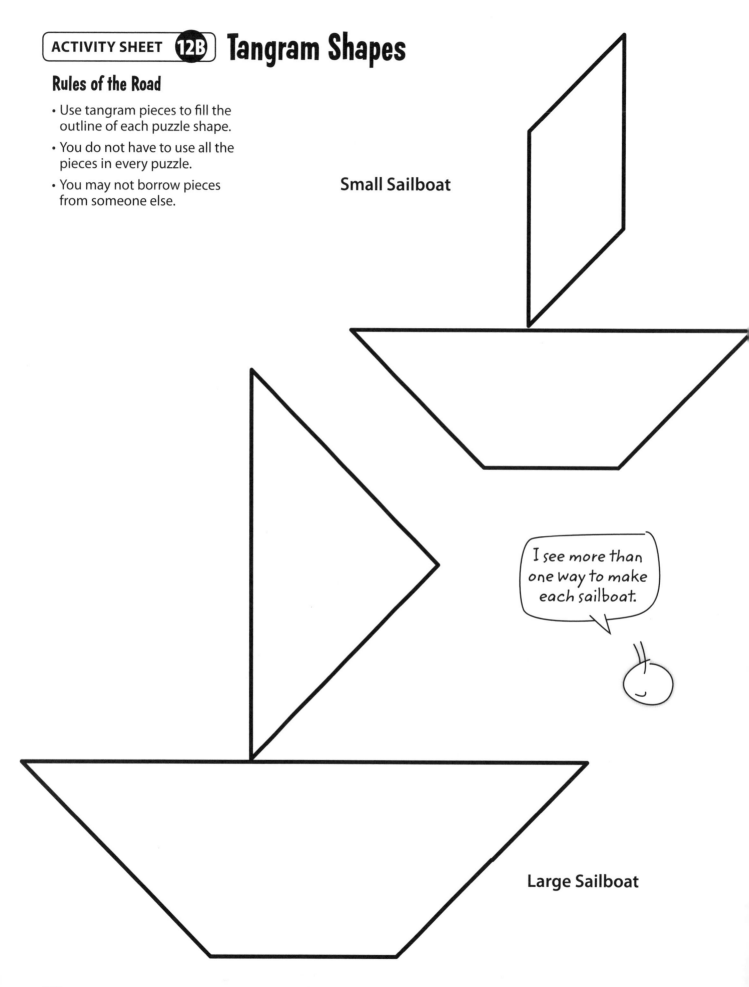

Small Sailboat

I see more than one way to make each sailboat.

Large Sailboat

Every Child Can Do Math © Crystal Springs Books

Tangram Shapes

Rules of the Road

• Use tangram pieces to fill the outline of each puzzle shape.

• You do not have to use all the pieces in every puzzle.

• You may not borrow pieces from someone else.

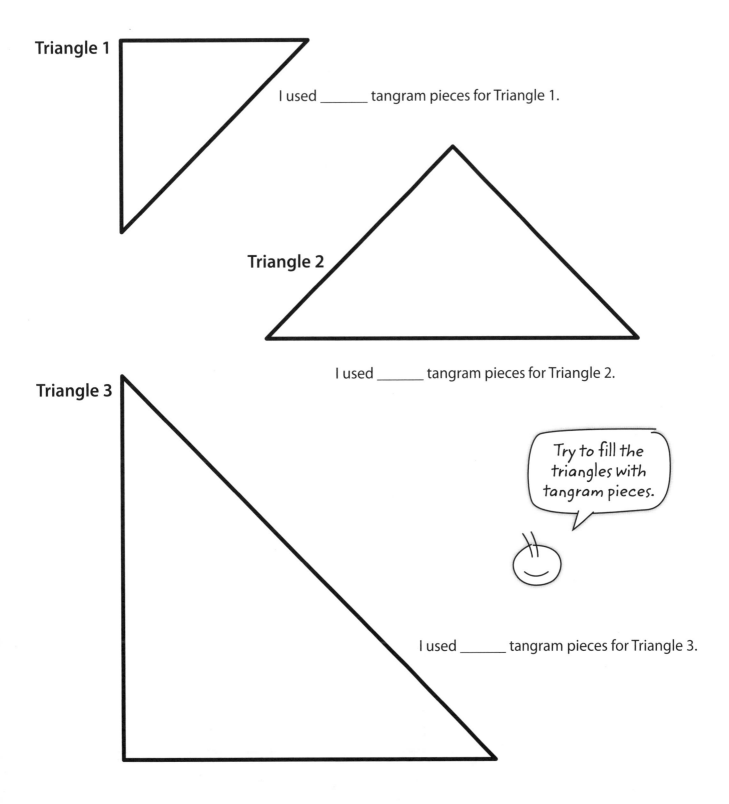

Triangle 1

I used _____ tangram pieces for Triangle 1.

Triangle 2

I used _____ tangram pieces for Triangle 2.

Triangle 3

Try to fill the triangles with tangram pieces.

I used _____ tangram pieces for Triangle 3.

Tangram Shapes

Rules of the Road

- Use tangram pieces to fill the outline of each puzzle shape.
- You do not have to use all the pieces in every puzzle.
- You may not borrow pieces from someone else.

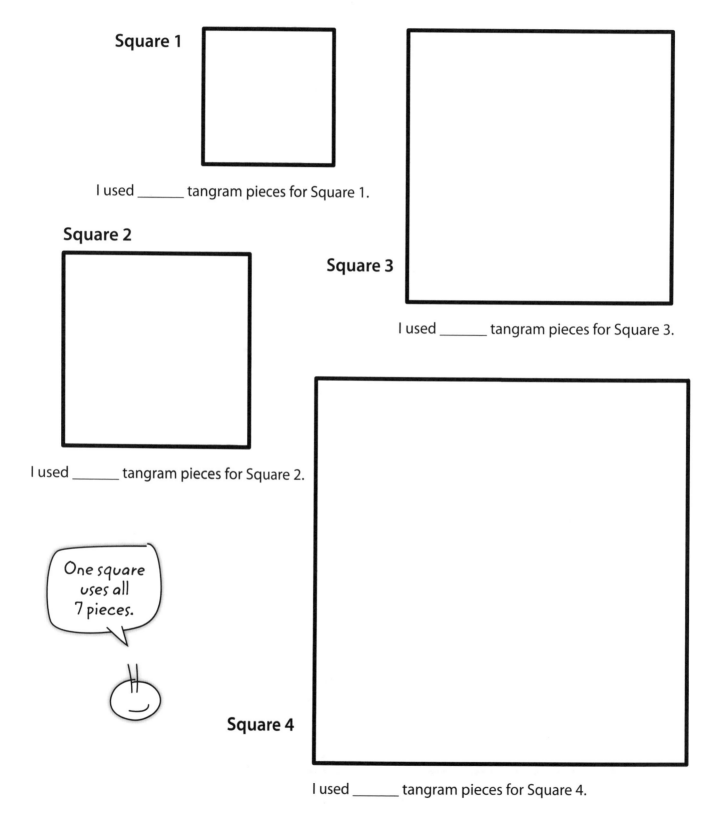

Square 1

I used _____ tangram pieces for Square 1.

Square 2

I used _____ tangram pieces for Square 2.

Square 3

I used _____ tangram pieces for Square 3.

One square uses all 7 pieces.

Square 4

I used _____ tangram pieces for Square 4.

Tangram Shapes

Rules of the Road

• Use tangram pieces to fill the outline of each puzzle shape.

• You do not have to use all the pieces in every puzzle.

• You may not borrow pieces from someone else.

Trapezoid 1

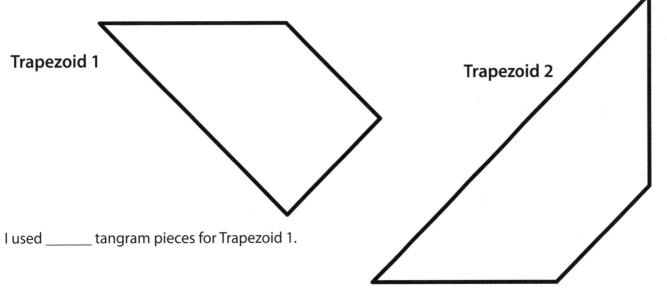

I used _____ tangram pieces for Trapezoid 1.

Trapezoid 2

I used _____ tangram pieces for Trapezoid 2.

Trapezoid 3

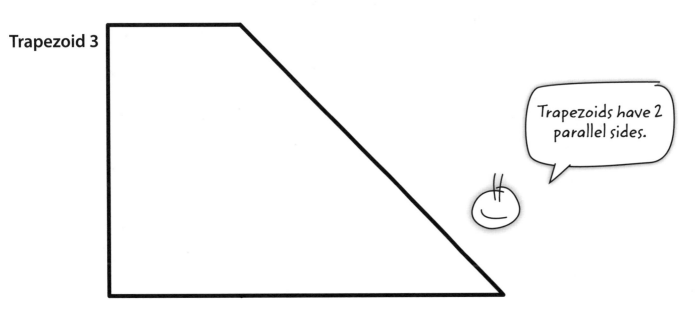

Trapezoids have 2 parallel sides.

I used _____ tangram pieces for Trapezoid 3.

ACTIVITY ⓭ Imagining Area

Why Do This Activity?

In Activity 13, students explore area. You will ask students to visualize a shape in their minds and to form that shape with manipulatives, given only oral directions. This is a more difficult task than the ones in Activities 11 and 12; in those activities, the outlines of the final figures were provided.

In this activity, students also debate the meaning of *size* and discover that figures can have different shapes but the same area. They discover how to visualize dividing complicated shapes into smaller, more familiar shapes that they can mentally "cut and paste" to find area more easily. Students apply their visualization skills by drawing shapes with a given area.

Prior Knowledge: basic geometric shapes, area

Academic Vocabulary: attribute, area, square, rectangle, triangle, quadrilateral, polygon, square unit

Time: 10 minutes for Level 1; up to 20 minutes each for Levels 2 & 3

Materials & Preparation:

- 1 set of 20 square tiles of the same size for each student

- Pencil, eraser, and ruler for each student

- Activity Sheets 13A and 13B, 1 copy of each for each student (pages 119–120)

- Document camera or other method of displaying and drawing on a dot grid during discussion

Activity Sheet **13A**

Activity Sheet **13B**

Guided Conversation

For Level 1, each student needs a set of 20 square tiles, all the same size. One-inch foam squares work well, but the tiles may be almost any size or material. For students who struggle, make sure that each set has only one color because multiple colors may distract students from the main concept.

Hand out the sets of square tiles and give students a couple of minutes to handle them. Then ask:

- *How would you describe the shape of these tiles? What are the attributes of this shape?*

Explain to students that you are going to describe some squares and rectangles, and they will build the shapes you describe. Ask:

- *Can you make a square that is 4 times the size of one tile?* (If your students have already learned the term, you may wish to use *area* from the beginning.)

Tell students to leave the square they just made on the table.

- *Can you use more tiles to make a square that is 4 times the size of the square you just made?*

Tell students they may take apart the shapes they just made and use the tiles for the next set of questions. Ask:

- *Can you use tiles to make a square that is 3 times the size of one tile?*
- *Can you use tiles to make a rectangle that is 3 times the size of one tile?*
- *How many ways can you make this rectangle?*
- *Can you use your tiles to make a rectangle that is 6 times the size of one tile?*
- *Can you make this rectangle another way?*

This next set of questions prompts students to compare the two rectangles they just made. Ask:

- *Do these two rectangles have the same shape?*

Behind the Math

Students should recognize that the tiles are squares. They should describe the attributes of a square: 4 sides of the same length and 4 right angles.

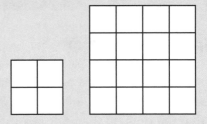

No; a square that is 3 times the size of one tile would take three square tiles, which won't make a square.

There is only one way to make this rectangle.

There are two rectangles that are 6 times the size of 1 tile.

No, the two rectangles have different shapes.

Guided Conversation *continued*

- *Are these two rectangles the same size? Explain your thinking.*

(Give students time to discuss this. Some will disagree that the two shapes are the same size. Let them explain their thinking to each other. Listen for explanations about differences in length and width, and about similarities in the number of tiles that make up each rectangle. This discussion will do more to promote student understanding than any explanation you can give.)

- *How are these two rectangles alike? Explain your thinking.*

If you plan to go on to Levels 2 and 3, introduce or review the term *area* and the concept of *square units*.

Behind the Math

It's hard to say whether the two rectangles are the same size because *size* describes more than one dimension. One rectangle is *longer* than the other, but the other is *wider*.

The two rectangles are alike because they are both made out of 6 tiles. That is, they both have the same *area*, which is 6 square units.

ACTIVITY 13 Imagining Area: LEVEL 2

Guided Conversation

Make sure everyone has a pencil, an eraser, and a ruler. Give each student a copy of Activity Sheet 13A. Tell students that the dots on the grids are 1 unit apart. In the first grid, have them draw a square that is 1 unit on a side and another one that is 2 units on a side. Ask:

- *Can you describe the area of each square?*

Next, point out the triangles in Grids 2 and 3. Ask:

- *What is the area of the triangle in Grid 2?*
- *What is the area of the triangle in Grid 3?*
- *Can you show how you know your answers are correct?* (Give students lots of time to talk about this and to explain their thinking to each other. Student discussions and demonstrations are more important than just knowing the correct answer in developing students' visualization.)

Behind the Math

A square with a side of 1 unit has an area of 1 square unit; a square with a side of 2 units has an area of 4 square units. (If the question of real measurements comes up, explain that for this activity the actual value of the unit isn't important.)

The triangles in Grids 2 and 3 both have areas of 2 square units.

You can demonstrate that the area of each triangle equals 2 square units by cutting each triangle and rotating the pieces to form a rectangle with an area of 2 square units.

It may help to prove the areas using scissors at first, but the goal is for students to visualize the smaller shapes that make up the larger ones and to use this information to solve area, without actually cutting or drawing on the shapes.

Guided Conversation *continued*

If students are having trouble visualizing the area of the triangles, say that Our Friend will tell them how he thinks about this.

Cut and paste!

When students are ready to work with the areas of shapes that include lines on a diagonal, ask them to find the areas of the figures in Grids 4 through 9 on Activity Sheet 13A.

If you feel students need more help with visualizing how to "cut and paste" the shapes, suggest they use scissors to cut the larger triangles into smaller shapes and then rearrange them into rectangles.

Grid 4—8 square units
Grid 5—6 square units
Grid 6—12 square units
Grid 7—$2\frac{1}{2}$ square units
Grid 8—9 square units
Grid 9—All 3 triangles have an area of 6 square units.

ACTIVITY 13 Imagining Area: LEVEL 3

Guided Conversation

Make sure everyone has a pencil, eraser, and ruler. Give each student a copy of Activity Sheet 13B. Guide students through the following questions.

- *How many squares total can you draw in the first grid?* (Give students time to work on this before moving on to the discussion below. Be prepared for the person who gives a quick answer of 1 or 16 squares. Tell her to keep looking without giving feedback on her answer.)

When students appear to be slowing down, invite answers. Some students may say "1 square" or "16 squares." If so, ask if squares can have different areas, then take another answer. Keep taking answers from students, asking if anyone found more squares, until someone gives a total of 30 squares. Invite a student to draw these squares on the grid where everyone can see them. Use a different color for squares of each area to help make the overlapping squares visible.

Behind the Math

There are 30 squares total:
16 have an area of 1 square unit (side length = 1 unit)
9 have an area of 4 square units (side length = 2 units)
4 have an area of 9 square units (side length = 3 units)
1 has an area of 16 square units (side length = 4 units)

Guided Conversation

Review the definition of *quadrilateral*, and then ask:

- *How many different quadrilaterals can you draw that have an area of 5 square units? Draw one shape per grid. Make sure each line you draw connects at least two dots.*

Give students time to explore this question, and then ask them to share answers. Next ask:

- *Are any of your quadrilaterals squares or rectangles?*

- *Can you draw any polygons other than quadrilaterals that have an area of 5 square units?*

Imagining Area

Rules of the Road

- Find the area of the shape in each grid.
- Write down the area in square units.

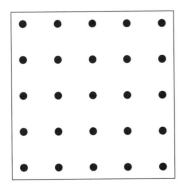

Grid 1 _____ square units

Grid 1 _____ square units

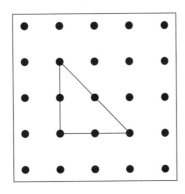

Grid 2 _____ square units

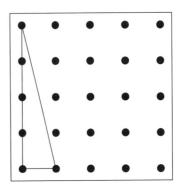

Grid 3 _____ square units

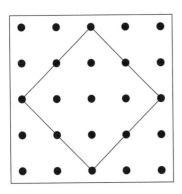

Grid 4 _____ square units

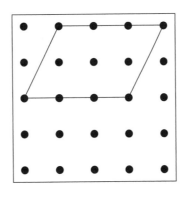

Grid 5 _____ square units

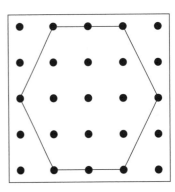

Grid 6 _____ square units

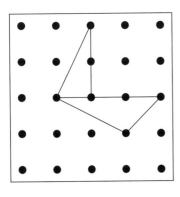

Grid 7 _____ square units

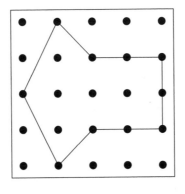

Grid 8 _____ square units

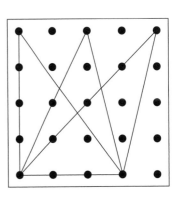

Grid 9 _____ square units

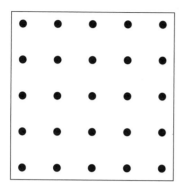
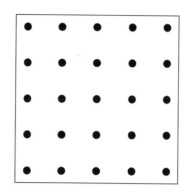
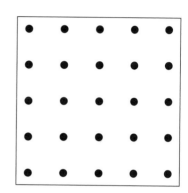

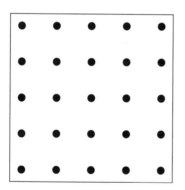
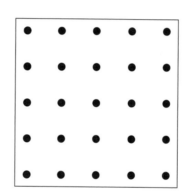
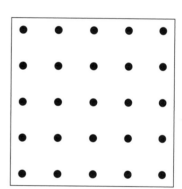

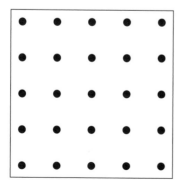
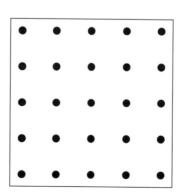
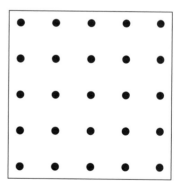

Every Child Can Do Math © Crystal Springs Books

ACTIVITY **14** Building Solids

Why Do This Activity?

This activity takes visualization right off the page, giving students three different visualization workouts. First, students visualize 3-dimensional objects from 2-dimensional drawings; then they build the 3-dimensional objects; and then they discover that the same object can look like a different object if it's drawn from a different angle. Along the way, they define some terms in 3-dimensional geometry, look for patterns, and test whether the patterns hold true (not always!).

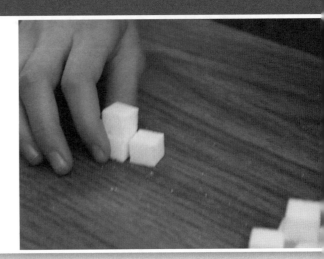

Prior Knowledge: addition, basic geometric shapes

Academic Vocabulary: cube, solid, rectangular solid (rectangular prism), faces of a solid, 2-dimensional, 3-dimensional

Time: 10–15 minutes each for Levels 1, 2 & 3

Materials & Preparation:

- 1 set of 10 or more cubes of the same size for each student

- Activity Sheets 14A and 14B, 1 copy of each for each student (pages 126–127)

- A board, document camera, or other method of displaying information where everyone can see it during discussion

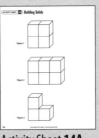

Activity Sheet **14A**

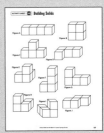

Activity Sheet **14B**

Guided Conversation

It is important that all students have cubes to work with, and that the cubes in each set all be the same size. Also, some students may find it easier to work with cubes that are all the same color.

Before you begin, you may wish to spend some time with your class discussing how a 2-dimensional drawing relates to the 3-dimensional object it shows. Give each student a copy of Activity Sheet 14A and at least 10 cubes. Ask students to use the cubes to build the shapes shown in Figures 1 and 2. After everyone has been successful, tell students that these figures are examples of *rectangular solids*, which are also called *rectangular prisms*. Ask:

- *What do these two figures have in common? How are they alike?* (If someone mentions the "sides," tell them these are called *faces*. Make sure students count all 6 faces.)

- *Can you guess what some properties of rectangular solids might be?* (Students may not yet understand all the properties. That's okay; they're about to learn more as they see another example.)

As students describe various properties, write a list where everyone can see it. When students have stopped adding properties to the list, have them use their set of cubes to build Figure 3 on Activity Sheet 14A. Ask:

- *How is Figure 3 like Figures 1 and 2? How is it different?* (If no one suggests it, guide students to count the number of faces on Figure 3.)

Tell students that Figure 3 is *not* a rectangular solid. Point out the list of the properties of a rectangular solid, then ask:

- *Do we want to make any changes to our list, based on the new information we have about Figure 3?* (Your list may or may not need changing, but go through each property and compare it to Figure 3 to test the list.)

Behind the Math

Thinking in 3 dimensions can be difficult, even for capable students. Expect that some students may require more time and support than others, when working on these activities.

At this point, accept all reasonable answers. Students may mention that both figures are made of cubes, have "square" edges (right angles), and have 6 flat sides (faces). They may also mention color, texture, and size—those properties aren't relevant, but students don't know that yet.

A rectangular solid (prism) has exactly 6 faces, and all faces are rectangles.

Accept all reasonable descriptions. Students may say that all three figures are made of cubes and have flat sides (faces), and that Figure 3 "has a corner" or "bends," while Figures 1 and 2 are straight. Figure 3 has 8 faces rather than 6.

Guided Conversation *continued*

- *Can we write a good definition of a rectangular solid from our list?* (As needed, share additional examples to omit properties that are not relevant, such as color or material.)

Tell students to take apart the figures they just made. They're going to use their sets of cubes to make new 3-dimensional solids based on the following questions. Ask:

- *How many rectangular solids with different shapes can you make with 4, 5, 6, 7, or 8 cubes?*

Either have everyone find out how many rectangular solids can be formed with each number of cubes, or you may prefer to assign groups of students a different number of cubes to test.

When students think they have found all possible solids for each number of cubes, invite students to share what they found. Tell students that if two figures have the same shape but are just positioned differently on the table, then they count as the same rectangular solid. Record your answers on a chart like the one at right.

When the chart is complete, ask:

- *Do you see a pattern in the results?*
- *Do you have a theory about the number of rectangular prisms you can make given a certain number of cubes?*

Encourage students to work in groups to test their theories using 9, 10, 11, and 12 cubes. Add results to the chart and discuss whether the pattern holds true for higher numbers of cubes.

Behind the Math

A rectangular solid (rectangular prism) has exactly 6 faces, and all faces are rectangles.

Number of Cubes	Number of Different Rectangular Solids
4	2
5	1
6	2
7	1
8	2

By looking at the numbers in the chart through 8 cubes, many students will predict that an odd number of cubes gives you 1 rectangular solid and an even number produces 2.

Number of Cubes	Number of Different Rectangular Solids
9	2
10	2
11	1
12	4

The even-odd theory works for 10 and 11 cubes, but it doesn't work for 9 and 12 cubes. It's an important lesson for students—they must thoroughly test any hypothesis they make.

Guided Conversation

There is no activity sheet for the Level 2 activities. Each student will need at least 10 cubes.

Tell students that they're going to use cubes to build stairs. Ask students to place one cube on the table. This represents a staircase with one step. Next, ask students to build a staircase of 2 steps. Follow this with 3 steps and then 4 steps, allowing plenty of time for each new task. Ask:

- *How many cubes did you need for each staircase?* (Draw a chart to record everyone's answers.)

- *Can you tell without building—just by looking at the chart—how many cubes you need to build a staircase with 5 steps?*

Have students look at the bottom row of cubes on the 4-step staircase. Ask:

- *How many cubes are in this bottom row?*

- *How many cubes are in each row above it?*

- *Think about those staircase rows. If your staircase needs 10 steps, what 10 numbers could you add together to get the total number of cubes in the staircase?*

Behind the Math

Number of Steps	Number of Cubes
1	1
2	3
3	6
4	10
5	?

A 5-step staircase takes 15 cubes (10 for 4 steps, plus 5 for the next step at the base of the staircase).

The bottom row has 4 cubes; the next ones up have 3 cubes, 2 cubes, and 1 cube.

For any staircase, add together the number of steps to get the number of cubes required.

So a 10-step staircase needs:
$10 + 9 + 8 + 7 + 6 + 5 + 4 + 3 + 2 + 1 = 55$ cubes

Guided Conversation

Give each student a copy of Activity Sheet 14B and 4 cubes.

Have students work in pairs to build each of the solids shown on the activity sheet, using only 4 cubes for each figure.

When everyone has completed the task, ask:

- *Were some figures harder to build than others?*
- *What made them seem harder?*

The next two questions explore the relationship between a 3-dimensional figure and a 2-dimensional drawing of the figure.

- *Do any of the drawings on the activity sheet show the same figure? How can you use your figures to prove this?*

- *Can you make a figure using more than 4 cubes that would match any of the pictures on the activity sheet?*

Behind the Math

Answers will vary, but some students may have found Figure E to be tricky because the drawing doesn't show the back of the figure.

Figures D, F, and G are the same figure drawn from different angles. Students can show this by rotating the 3-dimensional figure into each position. Note that Figures H and I look similar, but they are mirror images of each other. Rotating Figures H and I proves that they are not the same figure.

Figure B could be made with 5 cubes, and it would look the same if drawn from the same point of view. A student may name another figure; if she can explain her thinking, accept her answer.

Building Solids

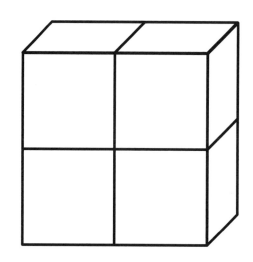

Figure 1

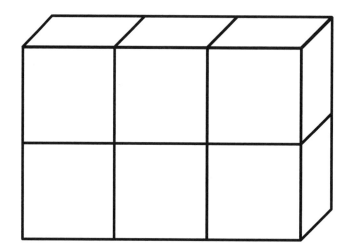

Figure 2

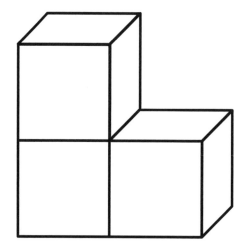

Figure 3

Every Child Can Do Math © Crystal Springs Books

Building Solids

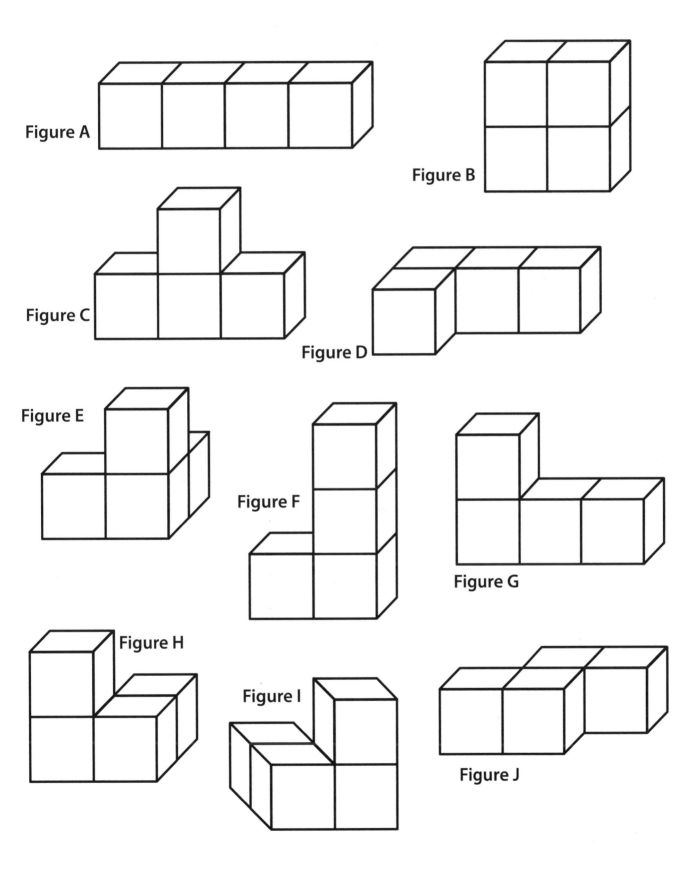

Figure A

Figure B

Figure C

Figure D

Figure E

Figure F

Figure G

Figure H

Figure I

Figure J

ACTIVITY 15 Broken Solids

Why Do This Activity?

Being able to imagine things that aren't really there is what this activity is all about. Students put their visualization skills to the test when they build rectangular solids based on incomplete 3-dimensional drawings.

Prior Knowledge: addition, basic geometric shapes

Academic Vocabulary: cube, solid, rectangular solid (rectangular prism), faces of a solid, 2-dimensional, 3-dimensional

Rules of the Road

• Figure out how many cubes were in each solid before the mice ate it.

• Write down how many cubes were in each solid.

Time: 10 minutes for Level 1; up to 15 minutes for Level 2

Materials & Preparation:

• 30 or more cubes of the same size for each student

• Activity Sheets 15A and 15B, 1 copy of each for each student (pages 131–132)

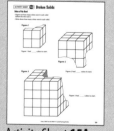

Activity Sheet **15A**

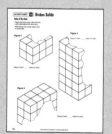

Activity Sheet **15B**

Guided Conversation

Give each student a copy of Activity Sheet 15A. Tell students that Our Friend Yuki made the solids shown on this sheet by gluing sugar cubes together. But then some hungry mice found them! The drawings on the activity sheet show what was left of these solids after the mice finished nibbling. Tell students that all of the solids started out as cubes. Ask:

- *What is a cube?*

Give each student 30 cubes, or set a container of cubes where a group can share. Any size cube will work for this activity.

Tell students to find the number of sugar cubes Our Friend used to build each solid and record their answers.

Give students plenty of time to work on this. Have students work in pairs if they are struggling, or if they need more cubes for Figure 3. When everyone has finished, ask:

- *Look at the picture of Figure 1. Can you tell from the picture how many faces are still a complete square?*

- *How many small squares would have been visible on Figure 2 before the mouse ate it, if you looked at all 6 faces?*

- *Is the number of small squares on the faces the same as the number of sugar cubes needed to build the solid? Can you explain why this is the case?*

Behind the Math

A cube is a solid with 6 faces, and all the faces are squares.

Figure 1 had 8 sugar cubes.
Figure 2 had 27 sugar cubes.
Figure 3 had 64 sugar cubes.

Notice that students are not being asked to build the original solids. They may do so, but if a student can find the correct answer without building the figure, this is a sign that the student has strong visualization skills.

At least 2 faces are intact squares. It is not possible to tell from this drawing if the base of Figure 1 is still a square.

Each face has 9 squares and the cube has 6 faces, so $9 \times 6 = 54$ squares.

No; there are more faces than cubes, because each cube has 6 faces.

Guided Conversation

Give each student a copy of Activity Sheet 15B. Explain that the mice also liked these rectangular solids, also known as rectangular prisms. Ask:

- *What is the difference between a cube and a rectangular solid?*

Ask students to find and write down the total number of sugar cubes Our Friend originally used to build each solid. When students are finished, ask:

- *Was this harder or easier than the cubes? Why?*

- *Can you tell from the picture how many faces on Figure 4 are still complete?*

- *How many faces are still complete on Figure 5?*

- *How many small squares (the sides of the sugar cubes) were visible on each of the 6 faces of Figure 5 before it was eaten my the mouse?*

Behind the Math

The faces of a cube must be squares, but the faces of a rectangular solid may be rectangles.

Figure 4 had 12 sugar cubes.
Figure 5 had 36 sugar cubes.
Figure 6 had 24 sugar cubes.

It may seem harder to know how many squares are on each face on a rectangular solid than on a cube.

Figure 4 has at least 2 complete faces, one with 6 squares and one with 4 squares. It is not possible to tell from this picture if the base of Figure 4 is intact.

Figure 5 has only 1 complete face showing, with 18 squares.

Two faces had 18 squares visible; 2 faces had 12 squares visible; and 2 faces had 6 squares visible.

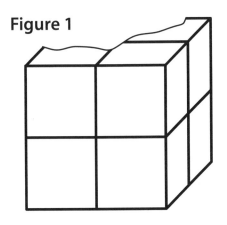

Rules of the Road

• Figure out how many cubes were in each solid before the mice ate it.

• Write down how many cubes were in each solid.

Figure 1

Figure 1 had _____ cubes to start.

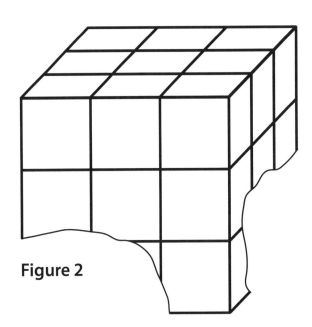

Figure 2

Figure 2 had _____ cubes to start.

Figure 3

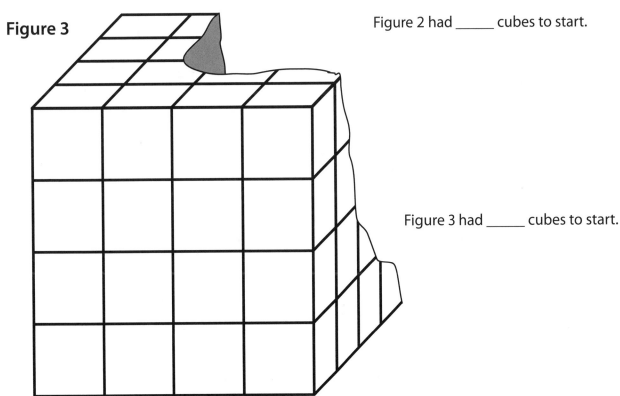

Figure 3 had _____ cubes to start.

Broken Solids

Rules of the Road

• Figure out how many cubes were in each solid before the mice ate it.

• Write down how many cubes were in each solid.

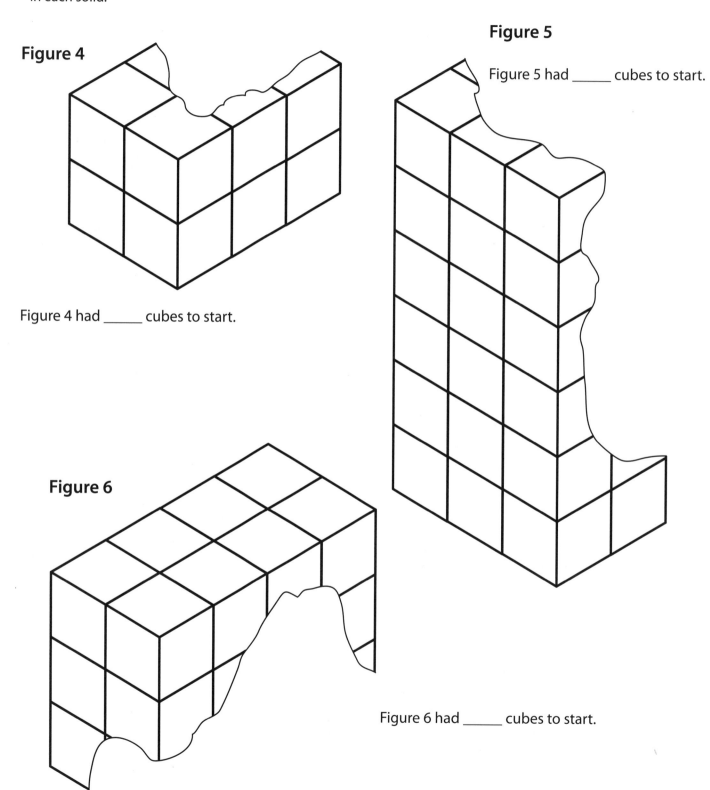

Figure 4

Figure 4 had _____ cubes to start.

Figure 5

Figure 5 had _____ cubes to start.

Figure 6

Figure 6 had _____ cubes to start.

Every Child Can Do Math © Crystal Springs Books

ACTIVITY ⑯ What I See from Here

Why Do This Activity?

Visualization skills get a workout as students build 3-dimensional models based on 2-dimensional pictures. They then view their models from various directions to confirm that they have built the figures in the drawings. Comparing figures with their neighbors lets students discover that different objects may look the same when viewed from certain directions. As with all visualization activities, the use of manipulatives in Activity 16 develops skills that students can later use to mentally manipulate solids, without building or viewing actual objects.

Prior Knowledge: 3-dimensional solids

Academic Vocabulary: faces (of solids), 2-dimensional, 3-dimensional

Rules of the Road

- Build figures in 3 dimensions, based on what they look like in 2 dimensions from different views.

- Compare and confirm interpretations.

Time: Up to 10 minutes each for Levels 1, 2 & 3

Materials & Preparation:

- 20 or more cubes of the same size for each student

- Activity Sheets 16A, 16B, and 16C, 1 copy of each for each student (pages 137–139)

- Document camera or other method of displaying activity sheets and materials during discussion

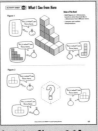

Activity Sheet **16A**

Activity Sheet **16B**

Activity Sheet **16C**

Guided Conversation

Give each student a copy of Activity Sheet 16A and about 20 cubes, or place a container of cubes where a group of students can share. Tell students that Our Friend Yuki is looking at solid figures made of cubes. When he looks directly at one side of a figure, the figure loses its 3-dimensional look and appears flat or 2-dimensional. The activity sheet shows what he sees when he looks from three different directions.

Ask students to use their cubes to build Figure 1 and then practice looking at it. They need to put their eyes at the level of the table and look at each side. Students need to have a sense of the 3-dimensional solid figure appearing flat or 2-dimensional when viewed from the side in order to complete the activity.

After everyone is familiar with the way Figure 1 looks from the sides, ask:

- *How many cubes did you need to build Figure 1?* (Ask at least 5 people what their answer is. If they don't agree, tell them, always with a smile, "Let's check it out together.")

- *Our Friend is going to look at Figure 1 from above. Can you draw what he will see?* (Give students time to work on this, and then invite a few volunteers to sketch their results.)

Next, point out Figure 2 on Activity Sheet 16A. Tell students that Figure 2 shows what Our Friend is seeing from different places, but it does not show Figure 2. Ask:

- *Can you build Figure 2 so that it matches what Our Friend is seeing?* (Give students time to do this.)

- *How many cubes did you need to build Figure 2?* (Keep calling on students until you get more than one answer. Do not say whether any answer is correct, yet.)

Behind the Math

In reality, students may still see the solid figures in 3 dimensions, due to lighting and good vision. If a student insists he can only see the figure in 3 dimensions, ask him to draw it in two dimensions as viewed from the side. That's the view he'll be working from to build solid figures, in this activity.

Figure 1 uses 14 cubes.

Top view of Figure 1

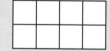

Figure 2 may be made using 6, 7, 8, 9, or 10 cubes.

Guided Conversation *continued*

Tell students to draw what their Figure 2 looks like when they look at it straight down from the top. Ask:

- *Does your Figure 2 match your neighbor's?* (Encourage students to compare solutions with several classmates.)

- *If you and your neighbor built different solids for Figure 2, can you both be correct? Explain your answer.* (Let students discuss this among themselves. Ask for responses from several students and discuss as a class.)

Behind the Math

Five possible views of top of Figure 2

Yes. Sometimes these solids, like Figure 2, will look different when viewed from the top; others will look the same from the top, as well as from the sides.

ACTIVITY 16 What I See from Here: LEVEL 2

Guided Conversation

Give each student a copy of Activity Sheet 16B and about 20 cubes, or place cubes where a group can share them. Invite students to use their cubes to build Figure 3. Ask:

- *How many cubes did you need to build Figure 3?*

- *Is your Figure 3 the same as your neighbor's? Can you have different solutions and both be right?* (Choose two students with different solutions, and ask each to convince you that their position is correct.)

- *Can you draw what Figure 3 looks like when you look straight down on it from the top?* (This view shows the differences among multiple correct solutions.)

Behind the Math

Students may have used 7, 8, or 9 cubes to build Figure 3.

The solution for Figure 3 can be built more than one way, as shown in the top-view pictures below.

Seven possible views of top of Figure 3

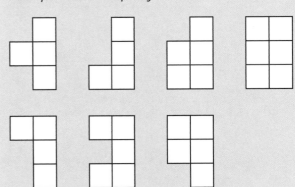

Guided Conversation *continued*

Call students' attention to Figure 4 on Activity Sheet 16B.
Ask:

- *Can you build Figure 4 using exactly 11 cubes?*
- *Can you build it using exactly 15 cubes?*
- *Can you draw what both solutions look like when you view them from the top?*

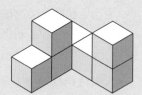

Figure 4 with 11 cubes   *Figure 4 with 15 cubes*

3 cubes high   3 cubes high

1 cube high   1 cube high

ACTIVITY 16 What I See from Here: LEVEL 3

Guided Conversation

Give each student a copy of Activity Sheet 16C and about
10 cubes. Point out that this time they have two side views
and a top view. Ask:

- *Can you build Figure 5 using only 8 cubes?*
- *Compare solutions with a neighbor. Can you have different solutions and both be right?*

- *Now use your cubes to build Figure 6. How many cubes did you use?*
- *Can you draw the other two sides of Figure 6?* (Remind students to draw 2-dimensional shapes to show how the figures appear when viewed straight on.)

Behind the Math

There is only one way to build Figure 5 using 8 cubes,
based on the drawings.

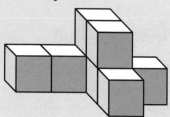

Figure 6 requires 7 cubes. Three variations of the solution
are shown.

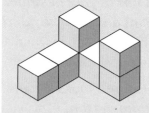

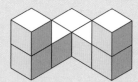

What I See from Here

Rules of the Road

- Build figures in 3 dimensions, based on what they look like in 2 dimensions from different views.
- Compare and confirm interpretations.

Figure 1

This is what I see from here.

This is what I see from here.

This is what I see from here.

Figure 2

This is what I see from here.

This is what I see from here.

This is what I see from here.

What I See from Here

Rules of the Road

- Build figures in 3 dimensions, based on what they look like in 2 dimensions from different views.
- Compare and confirm interpretations.

Figure 3

Figure 4

What I See from Here

Figure 5

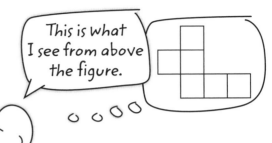

Rules of the Road

- Build figures in 3 dimensions, based on what they look like in 2 dimensions from different views.

- Compare and confirm interpretations.

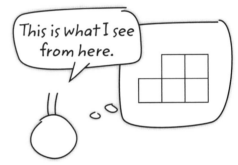

Figure 6

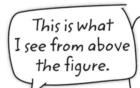

Activities 17–21

Patterns & Relationships

Making sense of a problem requires seeing patterns and relationships among numbers.

Patterns & Relationships

Throughout this book, we have been encouraging students to recognize patterns and relationships. Activities in Sections 1 and 2 have asked students to explore, make predictions, and test their ideas. Any time we've encouraged students to create an organized list of data or asked them to explore, explain, and discuss, we have been building this intellectual competency, as well as the competency of communicating ideas.

One question you can almost never overuse when discussing problems with your students is, "What do you notice?" Get them looking for patterns in numbers and shapes. Get them talking about what they think will happen next in a series. Students need to be willing to make predictions and know that they will be expected to thoroughly test their hypotheses and explain their thinking. Sometimes, their first idea won't end up working—and that's okay. The point is to get students to develop the habit of looking for patterns and relationships, testing their solutions, and trying until they find an idea that works.

Why Do Patterns and Relationships Matter?

Sam and Reena's teacher has shown them the following series of symbols.

∞ ☺ ◇ △ ∞ ☺ ◇ △ ∞ ☺ ◇ △ . . .

Sideways 8 is next!

When the teacher asks what symbol is next, Sam quickly raises his hand and answers, "Sideways 8 is next!" His teacher confirms he is right, and Sam smiles. But his smile is replaced with a crinkled brow when his teacher asks, "What symbol will be 99th in this series?" Sam grabs his pencil. But he's drawn only two or three more symbols when Reena raises her hand and says, "The 99th symbol will be a diamond!" Their teacher says Reena's answer is correct. Sam is shocked. He doesn't have a clue how Reena figured this out.

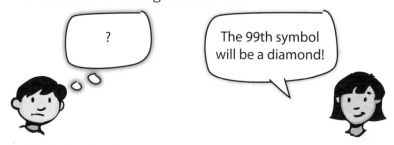

?

The 99th symbol will be a diamond!

Sam thinks back to another day when their teacher was writing numbers in a chart. The teacher asked them to look at the numbers in both columns and then figure out what the next output number would be.

Input Number	2	4	6	8	9
Output Number	10	30	50	70	?

Sam remembers that he didn't understand what to do. He kept thinking, "Where does it tell me what to do? Should I add, subtract, multiply, or divide? How can I tell?" Sam also remembers that, once again, Reena gave the answer—80. Reena explained that if you took the first number in any row, subtracted 1, then multiplied the result by 10, you'd get the second number.

Sam feels lost because he hasn't yet developed the habit of looking for patterns and relationships. Reena likes looking for patterns. She organizes information and looks at it until she discovers patterns among the numbers. This habit gives any student a strong foundation for algebraic thinking.

ACTIVITY SHEET 17

Patterns in Area & Perimeter

Figure 1

Figure 2

Figure 3

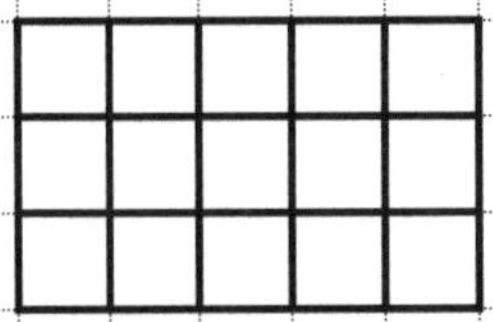

Figure 4

Figure 5

Figure	Area in Square Units (u^2)	Perimeter in Units (u)
1		
2		
3		
4		
5		

ACTIVITY **18** Name Patterns

Why Do This Activity?

In this activity, students practice looking for patterns in organized charts. By getting students to talk about what they think will happen next in a series of numbers, or by having them discover connections between numbers and patterns, you help them develop algebraic thinking skills. In addition to looking for patterns and making predictions based on those patterns, students find that it is important to test their theories. They also learn that they can use patterns as a shortcut to find answers—saving themselves the trouble of calculating an answer.

Prior Knowledge: division, odd and even numbers

Academic Vocabulary: multiples, remainder, consecutive numbers

Time: 10 minutes for Level 1; 15 minutes for Level 2; up to 20 minutes for Level 3

Materials & Preparation:
- Graph paper or lined paper for each student
- Pencils

Guided Conversation

Begin this activity using a name that has fewer than
5 letters in it and in which no letters are repeated. Don't
use the name of someone in the class just yet—save those
in case you want students to do this activity using their
own names as a follow-up.

It will help students keep the numbers on their charts lined
up under each letter if they use graph paper or lined paper
turned sideways so the lines become vertical on the paper.

Write "SAM" where all students can see it. Say that Sam is
writing numbers under the letters in his name. He writes
1 under the S, 2 under the A, 3 under the M, and then he
goes back to the beginning and writes 4 under the S. He
continues in this manner and ends up with a chart that
looks like this.

S	A	M
1	2	3
4	5	6
7	8	9
10	11	12
13	14	15

Draw the chart for your students, and then ask:

- *Do you see a pattern in the numbers in any of the
  columns in the chart?* (Remember to call on several
  students.)

- *Does the same pattern occur in every column?*
  (Encourage students to describe the patterns in all
  three columns.)

Once students have described a pattern, ask:

- *Are the numbers in all the columns multiples of 3?*

- *What is true of every number in the chart that is a
  multiple of 3?*

- *Without filling in the chart, can you figure out under
  which letter in Sam's name the number 21 will appear?
  How do you know?*

- *Did anyone figure this out a different way?*

Behind the Math

The numbers are increasing by 3 as you go down each
column, but the patterns are different in each.

Starting in the second row, the *S* column contains multiples of 3 plus 1 more. The *A* column contains multiples
of 3 plus 2 more. The *M* column contains multiples of 3.
Only the numbers in the *M* column are multiples of 3.
Every multiple of 3 falls in the *M* column.

The number 21 would fall in the *M* column, since it is an
even multiple of 3.

Guided Conversation *continued*

How would you describe the columns of numbers in terms of even and odd numbers?

Tell students that Mary told Sam she thinks the number 50 will be under the S.

- *Is Mary right? Why do you think so?*

ACTIVITY ⓘ Name Patterns: LEVEL 2

Guided Conversation

Tell students that, next, they'll use the same technique, but they'll make a chart for Sam's friend Veronica. Ask students to complete a chart for Veronica on their papers by first writing the name and then filling in numbers from 1 to 25. When students have finished their charts, ask:

- *How many complete rows did you fill in with numbers?*
- *How many numbers are written in the next row?*
- *In which row do you think the number 42 will land? Why do you think so?* (Give students time to work on this before modeling the division problem shown at right.)
- *What letter will 42 fall under?*

- *In which row do you think the number 1,524 will end up? What letter will 1,524 be under?* (Encourage a student to demonstrate how to solve this problem, using the same approach you just modeled for the number 42.)

Behind the Math

V	E	R	O	N	I	C	A
1	2	3	4	5	6	7	8
9	10	11	12	13	14	15	16
17	18	19	20	21	22	23	24
25							

Three rows are completely filled and one number is written in the next row.

Five rows would be filled and 2 numbers written in the next row. So 42 is in the sixth row under the letter *E*. One solution you can model for your students is to write out this division problem, and point out how each part of it helped you figure out where the number 42 would go. Your goal is for students to see the correlation between this answer and the division problem.

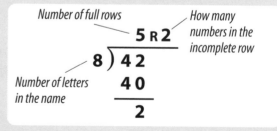

Using the same approach as above, divide 1,524 by 8 to get 190 R4. The number 1,524 will be under the letter *O* in the 191st row.

Guided Conversation *continued*

Ask students:

- *Do you notice anything about the numbers as you look down each column in VERONICA?* (If students have trouble, draw Our Friend Yuki and tell students his hint.)

Odds & evens

- *Did this happen when we used Sam's name? Can you figure out the difference?*

Behind the Math

The columns in the VERONICA chart are either all odd numbers or all even numbers.

No, the SAM chart had alternating odd and even numbers. Names with an odd number of letters have alternating even and odd numbers in each column. Names with an even number of letters have all odd or all even numbers in the columns.

ACTIVITY 18 Name Patterns: LEVEL 3

Guided Conversation

Tell students that Cheryl uses a different approach to filling in her name chart with numbers. Draw Cheryl's chart where students can see it:

C	H	E	R	Y	L
1	2	3	4	5	6
11	10	9	8	7	
	12	13	14	15	16
	20	19	18	17	

- *Can you figure out the pattern Cheryl is following to fill in her chart?* (Give students plenty of time to think. Ask several students to share their ideas, and discuss them.)

- *Where will Cheryl write the numbers 21 and 22?*

- *How would you describe the columns of numbers in Cheryl's chart, in terms of evens and odds?*

Behind the Math

When Cheryl gets to the end of a row, she reverses direction (or "turns around") but skips the first letter in the next row.

Following this pattern, 21 goes under the letter *C*, and 22 goes under the letter *H*.

The numbers in the columns are either all odd (under the 1st, 3rd, and 5th letters of the name) or all even (under the 2nd, 4th, and 6th letters of the name).

Guided Conversation *continued*

- *Do you see a pattern in the way the numbers are increasing in each column? Is it the same pattern in each column?*

- *Under what letter will Cheryl write the number 99? How did you figure this out?* (Let students think about this first, and then draw Our Friend Yuki and share his hint.)

Don't compute—look!

Behind the Math

The numbers in the end columns differ by 10. The patterns in the consecutive numbers in all the columns are best described visually.

C	H	E	R	Y	L
1	**2**	**3**	**4**	**5**	**6**
11	**10**	**9**	**8**	**7**	
	12	**13**	**14**	**15**	**16**
21	**20**	**19**	**18**	**17**	
	22	**23**	**24**	**25**	**26**

Notice that, though the patterns in the consecutive numbers aren't the same in the middle columns, every other number in each middle column differs by 10.

Since 99 is an odd number, it must be written in column *C, E,* or *Y* in the CHERYL chart. Look at the ones digit in each of the numbers in these columns:

In the *C* column, the ones digit is always 1.
In the *E* column, the ones digit is always 3 or 9.
In the *Y* column, the ones digit is always 5 or 7.

By noticing patterns, and without doing any computation, we can conclude that Cheryl will write 99 in the E column.

ACTIVITY **19** Coin Patterns

Why Do This Activity?

In this activity, students practice looking for patterns in a series of visuals, and then they move on to look for patterns in the numbers that describe those visuals. Encouraging students to see connections between numbers and patterns helps them develop algebraic thinking skills, sometimes even before they've learned the term *algebra*. You may take advanced students beyond describing the pattern, to writing an algebraic expression for the pattern they've discovered.

Prior Knowledge: multiplication, square of a number

Academic Vocabulary: square of a number

Time: Up to 20 minutes for Level 1; up to 10 minutes each for Levels 2 & 3

Materials & Preparation:

- Activity Sheet 19, 1 copy for each student (page 157)
- Colored pencil or pen
- 100 or more pennies or bingo chips per student (optional)

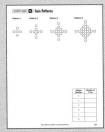

Activity Sheet 19

Guided Conversation

Give each student a copy of Activity Sheet 19. Actual coins are not needed, but if your students would benefit from manipulatives, place containers of pennies or bingo chips where groups of students may share them.

Tell students that the drawings on the activity sheet show coins that Our Friend Yuki arranged by following a rule he made up. Ask:

- *Can you figure out Our Friend's rule for the coin patterns, from looking at Patterns 1 to 4 on the activity sheet?*

Give students plenty of time to think before moving on. They need some idea of a pattern to test before they try building the next pattern in the series. If you see students still struggling after a good amount of time, suggest that they color in the 4 corner coins in each pattern, as shown below.

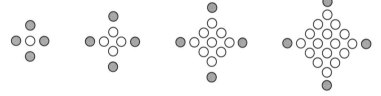

Give students more time to examine the patterns after coloring the corner coins; even then, do not explain the rule yet. Testing the rule themselves before being told whether it is correct is important for students who are developing their thinking skills.

When students think they have figured out the pattern, ask:

- *Can you build Pattern 5, the next one in the series?* (Wait before showing students the correct answer. It's more important for them to compare answers with each other.)

Have students compare drawings of Pattern 5 with their neighbors. Ask if they all agree. If they do not, suggest that they explain their thinking to each other. Then ask:

- *Do any of you want to change your drawing of Pattern 5 after talking with your neighbors?*

Behind the Math

Help students uncover the pattern by giving them the hints that follow.

Coloring the corners will help focus student attention on the non-colored coins in the drawings, which we'll refer to as the core coins. Notice that the number of core coins equals the square of the pattern number.

Pattern 1: 1×1 or 1
Pattern 2: 2×2 or 4
Pattern 3: 3×3 or 9
Pattern 4: 4×4 or 16

Our Friend's rule is to first make a square of coins using the square of the pattern number and then add 1 coin to each of the 4 corners.

Pattern 5 has a 5×5 square of core coins plus 1 coin on each corner.

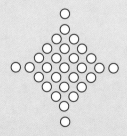

Accept all answers. The point is to encourage students to discuss the reasons they drew the patterns they did.

Guided Conversation

Ask students to figure out how many coins Our Friend used in each of the 5 patterns in Level 1. Have them write these numbers in the chart on their activity sheets. Once they've done this, ask:

- *Do you see a pattern in the number of coins as you go down the column?* (Keep in mind that different people may describe the pattern in different ways. Encourage students to share all explanations. Someone who doesn't want to speak up may have been thinking the same way, and that person needs to hear that his method was also valid.)

- *Based on that pattern, how many coins will be in Pattern 6 of the series?*

- *How did you figure this out?* (Encourage several students to explain their thinking.)

- *When you figured out the number of coins in each pattern, did anyone do something other than count each coin?* (Encourage all students to look for patterns in both the pictorial model on their activity sheet and in the abstract numbers in the chart.)

Behind the Math

Pattern Number	Number of Coins	
1	5	) 3
2	8	) 5
3	13	) 7
4	20	) 9
5	29	
6		

As shown above, the numbers are increasing by consecutive odd numbers:

Pattern 2 uses 3 more coins than Pattern 1.
Pattern 3 uses 5 more coins than Pattern 2.
Pattern 4 uses 7 more coins than Pattern 3.

And so forth . . .

Pattern 6 will have 40 coins. Here are two ways to figure this out.

Square the pattern number ($6 \times 6 = 36$), and then add 4 for the 4 corners of the pattern: ($36 + 4 = 40$ coins).

To the total number of coins for the last pattern (29), add the next consecutive odd number in the column pattern (11): ($29 + 11 = 40$ coins).

Students may have used one of the methods described above. Some students may have seen and used a pattern in the visual models. If they did, they may have found the total number of core coins, either by counting or finding the area, and then just added the 4 corner coins that are in each model.

Guided Conversation

In Level 3, students use Our Friend's pattern from Levels 1 and 2 to make more predictions and to describe some algebraic relationships.

- *Could Our Friend form a pattern in his series that uses exactly 50 coins? How do you know that?* (If students need help, suggest they add another column to their chart and then in that column, rewrite the number of coins as a number times itself [a number squared] plus 4.)

- *How many coins would Pattern 10 in the series use?*

- *Can you find this number without drawing the pattern on paper?*

If your students are doing well, see if they can translate Our Friend's pattern into an algebraic expression. If they need support, tell them you will help by translating what they say into mathematical symbols. When they say, "First you multiply the number by itself," you will write so everyone can see, "$n \times n$." Tell them you're letting "n" stand for the number so you don't have to keep writing it out.

Tell students that Our Friend Yuki wants to write an expression that would describe how many coins are needed for any pattern in the series.

- *If Our Friend lets n stand for any pattern number, can you write an expression that works for the pattern?*

Behind the Math

Our Friend can't use exactly 50 coins because 50 coins − 4 corner coins = 46, and 46 is not the square of any number.

Pattern 10 will use 104 coins:

$10 \times 10 = 100$ (core coins);
$100 + 4$ (corner coins) $= 104$ coins

If n equals any pattern number, then the expression for the total number of coins used is as follows:

$$(n \times n) + 4 \quad \text{or} \quad n^2 + 4$$

Pattern 1

Pattern 2

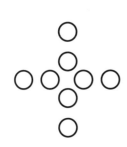

Pattern 3

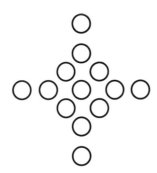

Pattern 4

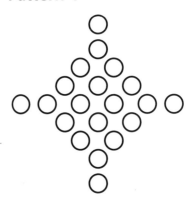

Pattern Number	Number of Coins
1	
2	
3	
4	
5	
6	

ACTIVITY 20 **Handshakes**

Why Do This Activity?

The handshake activity carries your students from experiencing a problem in concrete terms, to representing the same problem pictorially, to looking for patterns in an abstract representation of it. Along the way, they discover the value of diagrams and organized charts in solving even seemingly simple problems.

Prior Knowledge: how to organize information into charts

Academic Vocabulary: consecutive numbers, pattern

Time: 10 minutes for Level 1; up to 20 minutes for Level 2

Materials & Preparation:
- Paper
- Pencils
- 5 sticky labels numbered 1 to 5

Guided Conversation

Make sure each student has paper and a pencil. Then tell students to imagine that they are planning a meeting. At the meeting, everyone will shake hands with everyone else exactly once. Ask:

- *What is the fewest number of people you need at the meeting in order for 1 handshake to happen?*

Next, expand the process. Ask:

- *How many handshakes happen if 3 people are at the meeting?*

Tell students they're going to test their answers. Call three student volunteers to the front of the room. Ask the first person to shake hands exactly once with each of the other two people, while everyone else counts. Then ask the next person to do the same thing, but tell him to skip the person he already shook hands with. Finally, have the third person shake hands with anyone she hasn't shaken with yet.

Now, get the students really thinking. Ask:

- *How many handshakes will happen for 4 people?*

To find out, invite another volunteer up and repeat the process. Continue in this way for 5 people. Each time you add a person, have one volunteer at a time shake hands with each other person once, and have the rest of the class count handshakes. Tell the next volunteer to shake hands only with people she hasn't shaken with yet.

Ask the class:

- *Did you find it more difficult to keep track as more people arrived at the meeting?*
- *What would it be like if you tried to keep track of 20 people at the meeting?*

Behind the Math

You need at least 2 people for 1 handshake.

Three people make 3 handshakes happen.

Four people make 6 handshakes.

Five people make 10 handshakes.

By this point most students will recognize that it's impractical to test the number of handshakes if a meeting has more than a few people.

Guided Conversation *continued*

Point out that, as numbers get bigger in problems like this, it's difficult to find solutions by manipulating objects or counting handshakes. The good news is that there are other ways to solve these problems. Tell students it's time to look at the problem another way.

Ask five new volunteers to form a circle at the front of the room. Give each a sticky label (1, 2, 3, 4, or 5) to put on his shirt. Then write the numbers 1, 2, 3, 4, 5 in a circle where everyone can see it, as shown below.

1

5   **2**

4   **3**

Tell students that this time, you'll use this diagram to keep track of the handshakes. Ask Volunteer 1 to shake hands with each of the other people. Each time, she should say the number of the person she is shaking hands with. As each handshake happens, draw a line between the two numbers in the diagram. When Volunteer 1 finishes, ask Volunteer 2 to shake hands with anyone he hasn't yet shaken hands with. Continue in this manner, asking volunteers to shake hands with anyone they haven't shaken with yet. If they lose track, refer to the diagram.

Have the five volunteers return to their seats. Ask:

- *How many lines did we draw on the handshake diagram for 5 people? How many handshakes does the diagram show?*

- *Can you draw a similar diagram to show handshakes for a meeting of 6 people?* (After students have had time to work this out, invite someone to draw her solution on the board. Invite the class to count aloud as she draws the lines.)

Behind the Math

The goal here is for students to start transitioning from a concrete stage of modeling the problem (shaking hands) to a pictorial stage (a diagram) by seeing the connection between what is happening in the front of the room and the lines you will add to the drawing.

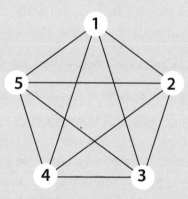

The 5-person diagram has 10 lines for 10 handshakes.

A 6-person diagram has 15 lines for 15 handshakes.

Guided Conversation

In Level 2, you'll be transitioning students from the pictorial diagram to a chart of organized information, which is an abstract level of understanding for this problem. Ask students:

- *Would drawing a diagram help answer the question about 20 people attending this meeting?*

Suggest to that class that organizing the information into a chart might be less messy and easier to understand. Create a chart for 2 to 10 people using the headings shown. Have students make this chart and fill in the first five rows based on the information you've already gathered.

Number of People at the Meeting	Number of Handshakes
2	1
3	3
4	6
5	10
6	15
7	
8	
9	
10	

Ask students:

- *Do you notice any pattern in the number of handshakes as you go down the column?* (Have students share their ideas, but do not yet confirm whether they are correct.)

- *Can you use the pattern you noticed to find out how many handshakes will happen with 7 people at the meeting?* (Call for solutions from several students. Write down all solutions, even the ones that repeat.)

Behind the Math

Most students will recognize that drawing all the lines to connect 20 numbers in a circle to all the other numbers in the circle would be time-consuming and messy, and the lines would be difficult to count.

The completed chart gives answers for the questions in the Guided Conversation. Do not share these answers with students; instead, use them to confirm the ideas and answers that students come up with and test on their own, during the Guided Conversation.

Number of People at Meeting	Number of Handshakes	
2	1	+
3	3	)2
4	6	)3
5	10	)4
6	15	)5
7	21	)6
8	28	)7
9	36	)8
10	45	)9

Guided Conversation *continued*

When student answers slow down, circle the answer "21." Ask:

- ***Can someone who gave this solution explain how he got it?*** (Be prepared for students to share more than one way to reach the correct answer. But also encourage students who have discovered the same pattern to share their results.)

When several students have described the pattern, have everyone apply this pattern to fill in the rest of the chart. When all students have finished, ask:

- ***Do you notice anything about the numbers in the Handshakes column?*** (Have Our Friend offer the hint "odds and evens" if students do not think of this after a minute or two.)

- ***If there are 25 people in the room, will there be an odd number of handshakes or an even number of handshakes?***

Have students who are interested figure out the question asked at the start of Level 2: How many unique handshakes will happen in a meeting of 20 people?

Behind the Math

The chart on page 161 shows the pattern. Some students may describe the pattern by saying that each row equals the previous number of handshakes, plus a consecutive whole number:

$$3 \text{ people: } 1 + 2 = 3$$
$$4 \text{ people: } 3 + 3 = 6$$
$$5 \text{ people: } 6 + 4 = 10$$
$$6 \text{ people: } 10 + 5 = 15$$

Thus, for 7 people you'd add the number 6: $15 + 6 = 21$ handshakes.

Students may also describe this pattern as the difference between each number and the next being consecutive numbers.

A pattern of "odd, odd, even, even" repeats down the column.

"Odd, odd, even, even" is a 4-place pattern. The last time that the pattern repeats in our chart is at 9 people. So one way to find the answer for 25 people is to subtract 9 from 25. That gives you 16, which means the pattern repeats 4 more times exactly. Therefore, 25 people would make an even number of handshakes, just like 9 people did. Remember that this is only one way to solve the problem. Your students may find many more!

Twenty people make 190 unique handshakes.

ACTIVITY **21** Sticks & Clay

Why Do This Activity?

In this activity, students solve a simple puzzle by looking for a fairly simple pattern, but you may choose to make the problem more or less challenging by the way you present it. Some students will do better if they begin with concrete manipulatives. Others may be ready to work with pictorial diagrams, while some will quickly progress to finding patterns in the abstract representation of the problem after a quick introduction to the diagram. Depending on your students' agility in mathematical thinking, you may show them how to arrange the information in order to look for patterns, or challenge them to figure out how to organize it for themselves.

Prior Knowledge: 1-digit division

Academic Vocabulary: square, pattern

Time: 10 minutes each for Levels 1, 2 & 3

Materials & Preparation:

- Paper and pencil for each student

- Toothpicks and clay balls or miniature marshmallows, 25 each for demonstration, or 25 each for each student (optional)

- Document camera or other method of displaying activity and materials during discussion

ACTIVITY **21** **Sticks & Clay:** LEVEL **1**

Guided Conversation

In Level 1, students look for a pattern in adjacent squares that are built from toothpicks and clay balls. You may lead this activity by building the squares yourself (or drawing them) while students watch. Alternatively, you may choose to have students make their own models using toothpicks and clay balls or miniature marshmallows. Either way, guide students through the following steps, asking questions and allowing time for discussion of student ideas.

Tell students you're going to use sticks (for the sides) and clay (for the corners) to make a square.

- *How many sticks do we need to make 1 square?*
- *How many clay balls will be used?*

After students answer, build the square. Then add on to the first square to make another square, as shown.

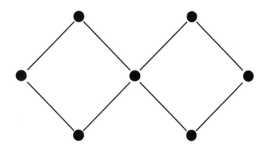

Ask these questions about the 2-square model:

- *How many squares are there?*
- *How many sticks were used?*
- *How many clay balls were used?*

Tell students to imagine themselves adding more squares to this model. Ask them to draw an organized chart to show how they'd do this. Tell them their chart needs to answer these questions for models with 1 to 6 squares:

- *How many sticks are used, in total, for each model?*
- *How many clay balls are used, in total, for each model?*

Behind the Math

One square uses 4 sticks and 4 clay balls.

The 2-square model has 2 squares. It uses 7 clay balls and 8 sticks.

Number of Squares	Number of Clay Balls	Number of Sticks
1	4	4
2	7	8
3	10	12
4	13	16
5	16	20
6	19	24

164 Activity 21 / Sticks & Clay / Level 1

Guided Conversation *continued*

If you've done other activities in this book that use organized charts, then see how many students can create the chart on their own. After a while, if some students are still struggling with how to begin, show them the headings needed for the chart and let them continue from there.

After all students have successfully drawn and completed a chart, ask:

- *Do you see any patterns in the way the numbers increase in each column of the chart?* (Encourage a number of students to share their observations for each column.)

Behind the Math

The number of sticks is 4 times the number of squares. Another way to say this is that the numbers in the sticks column are all multiples of 4.

The numbers in the clay balls column all differ by 3, but they are not multiples of 3. Be sure to ask students to explain the difference. Another way to say this is that you add 3 to the previous number of clay balls to get the next number.

ACTIVITY 21 Sticks & Clay: LEVEL 2

Guided Conversation

The discussion in Level 2 refers to the chart that students created in Level 1. Ask students to look at the numbers in the clay ball column of the chart. Ask:

- *What could you do to each of these numbers that would make each number a multiple of 3?*

Tell students that Our Friend wants to make 10 connected squares, but he needs to know if he has enough materials.

- *Without adding to your model or drawing, can you tell Our Friend how many sticks he needs?*
- *How many clay balls does Our Friend need to make 10 squares?* (If after a good amount of time you see students with unhappy eyes, offer Our Friend's hints.)

How many for Square 1?

How many more for each square after that?

Behind the Math

Subtracting 1 from each number would turn them all into multiples of 3. An alternative approach is to add 2 to each number in the column.

To make 10 squares, Our Friend needs 40 sticks and 31 clay balls.

You need 4 clay balls and 4 sticks for the first square. Each additional square takes 3 clay balls and 4 sticks.

Guided Conversation

Suppose you have 339 clay balls and an unlimited number of sticks.

- *How many squares could you make in a line series like this, using these materials?*

As needed, tell students that they may *not* plan to rework the clay into more balls to solve the problem.

- *Would you have any clay balls left over that you couldn't use to form a complete square?*

- *How many clay balls would you need to form 2,009 squares in a line like this?*

Behind the Math

Remember that the first square takes 4 clay balls. Each additional square takes 3 clay balls.

339 clay balls − 4 (clay balls used on first square) = 335
335 ÷ 3 (clay balls for each additional square) = 111 R2

This means that after you make the first square, you can make 111 more complete squares. You'll have 112 squares and 2 pieces of clay left over.

You need 3 clay balls for each square plus an additional clay ball for the first square. Set up the problem and solve it:

(number of squares × 3) + 1 = ? clay balls
(2,009 × 3) + 1 = ? clay balls
(6,027) + 1 = 6,028 clay balls

APPENDIX

Copymasters

Number Cards

Copy to cardstock, then cut out.

0	1	2	3
4	5	6	7
8	9	0	1
2	3	4	5
6	7	8	9

Pattern Blocks

Copy to cardstock, then cut out.

3 Hexagons Color these yellow, then cut out.

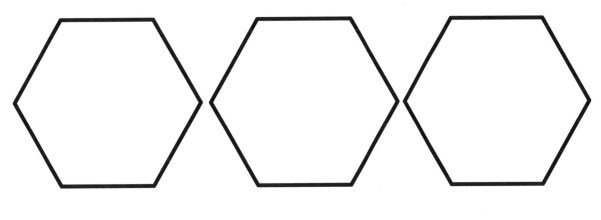

6 Trapezoids
Color these red,
then cut out.

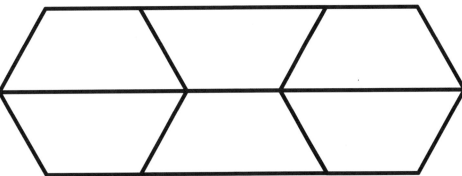

9 Rhombuses
Color these blue,
then cut out.

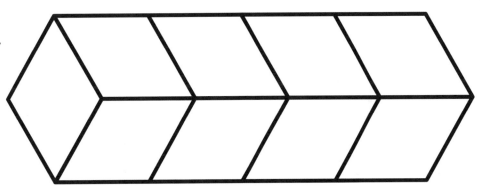

18 Triangles
Color these green,
then cut out.

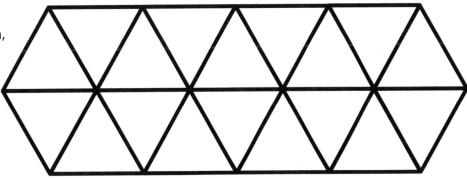

Tangram Set

Copy to cardstock, then cut out.

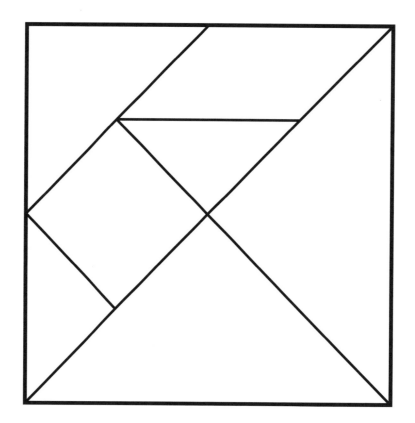

Every Child Can Do Math © Crystal Springs Books

References

Bruner, J. 2000. *The Process of Education*. Cambridge, MA: Harvard University Press.

Chen, S. 2008. *The Parent Connection for Singapore Math*. Peterborough, NH: Crystal Springs Books.

Dienes, Z. 1971. *Building Up Mathematics*. London: Hutchison Educational Limited.

Gibbons, P. 2002. *Scaffolding Language, Scaffolding Learning*. Portsmouth, NH: Heinemann.

Hazekamp, J. 2011. *Why Before How*. Peterborough, NH: Crystal Springs Books.

Johnston, P.H. 2004. *Choice Words*. Portland, ME: Stenhouse Publishers.

Keene, E.O., and S. Zimmermann. 1997. *Mosaic of Thought*. Portsmouth, NH: Heinemann.

Kuhns, C. 2006. *Number Wonders*. Peterborough, NH: Crystal Springs Books.

———. 2009. *Building Number Sense*. Peterborough, NH: Crystal Springs Books.

Lee, P.Y. (ed.). 2007. *Teaching Primary School Mathematics*. Singapore: McGraw-Hill.

Leinwand, S. 2009. *Accessible Mathematics*. Portsmouth, NH: Heinemann.

Ma, L. 1999. *Knowing and Teaching Elementary Mathematics*. Mahwah, NJ: Lawrence Erlbaum.

Ng Chye Huat, J. (Mrs.), and Mrs. Lim Kian Huat. 2001. *A Handbook for Mathematics Teachers in Primary Schools of Singapore*. Singapore: Federal Publications—Times Media Private Limited.

Parker, T., and S. Baldridge. 2003. *Elementary Mathematics for Teachers*. Bloomington, IN: Sefton-Ash Publishing.

Skemp, R. 2002. *Mathematics in the Primary School*. London: Routledge.

Van de Walle, J.A., K.S. Karp, and J.M. Bay-Williams. 2010. *Elementary and Middle School Mathematics: Teaching Developmentally, 7th edition*. San Francisco: Allyn & Bacon.

Vygotsky, L. 1978. *Mind in Society: The Development of Higher Psychological Processes*. Cambridge, MA: Harvard University Press.

Wegerif, R., and N. Mercer. 1996. "Computers and Reasoning Through Talk in the Classroom." *Language and Education* 10 (1): 47–64.

Other Products from Crystal Springs Books

Why Before How *Singapore Math Computation Strategies*
JANA HAZEKAMP

Your students know that 2 × 3 = 6, but do they know why? Do they have the mathematical reasoning skills to see them through more than just the next test? Jana explains how to walk students step-by-step through each strategy, connect that approach to others, and build true mathematical understanding.

(1–6) 128 pp. #402682

Step-by-Step Model Drawing *Solving Word Problems the Singapore Way*
CHAR FORSTEN

Model drawing offers a clear, pictorial approach to teaching logic, number relationships, and problem-solving. Char introduces the step-by-step process and helps you guide students in applying it to sample problems—providing examples ranging from simple addition to fractions, decimals, ratios, and rates. She follows up with plenty of extra problems—all fully reproducible—so your students can practice what they've learned.

(1–6) 144 pp. #402696

Model Drawing for Challenging Word Problems
Finding Solutions the Singapore Way
LORRAINE WALKER

Take your understanding of model drawing to the next level—extending the basic strategies and learning how to apply them to more complex problems. At the same time, you'll discover ways to incorporate questioning techniques into your model-drawing instruction so that you gain real insight into the depth of your students' understanding.

(6–9) 160 pp. #402698

Math Strategies You Can Count On
Tools & Activities to Build Math Appreciation, Understanding & Skills
CHAR FORSTEN

Your students will be eager for math class to begin when you implement these energizing activities. Learn how you can introduce more and more complex concepts by keeping things based in the concrete and visual while guiding students' discovery of patterns and relationships. Char offers fresh new ways to capture students' imaginations by showing them the math in what they already love.

(2–6) 128 pp. #454871

Place Value Disks BOB HOGAN

These easy-to-manipulate disks provide hands-on practice for developing number sense. Color coded according to place value, the 1-in. foam disks allow students to visually track what happens when they regroup numbers in both addition and subtraction. And they help illustrate that multiplication is the same as repeated addition, and division is the same as repeated subtraction.

(3–6) 140 disks (20 for each of 7 values) #402648

Crystal Springs
BOOKS
a division of Staff Development for Educators

To order, call 800-321-0401 or visit our website: www.SDE.com/crystalsprings.